YOGA
Touchstone

योगनिकषपाषाणम्

YOGA Touchstone

N.E. Sjoman & H.V. Dattatreya

BLACK LOTUS BOOKS INC.

Black Lotus Books Inc.
P.O. Box 70126, Bowness R.P.O.
Calgary, Alberta, Canada, T3B 5K3
www.blacklotusbooks.com

Library and Archives Canada Cataloguing in Publication

Sjoman, N.E.
Yoga touchstone / N.E. Sjoman and H.V. Dattatreya.

ISBN 0-9736162-0-2

1. Yoga, Hatha — History. 2. Yoga, Hatha. I. Dattatreya, H.V., 1959 – II. Title.

BL1238.52.S56 2004   613.7'046'09   C2004-904301-3

Technical Credits:
Design, Production & Print Management: Jeremy Drought, Last Impression Publishing Service, Calgary, Alberta
Cover & Interior Photographs: N.E. Sjoman
Printing: *Friesens Corporation*, Altona, Manitoba, CANADA

Author Note

Sanskrit terminology has been transcribed directly in Roman script without diacritical marks since this is not a text for Sanskrit specialists. Devanagari quotes are given only in the original devanagari. All photographs are of Sri Dattatreya taken by N.E. Sjoman in various places around the world.

ॐ नमो भगवते शिवाय।

श्री गुरुभ्यो नमः।

अभिवन्द्य गुरुनादौ शिष्यधीपद्मनीकरीन्।
तत्सत्सात्रान् करिष्येऽहं योगनिकषपाषाणम्॥

नच्चात्रातीव कर्तव्यं दोषदृष्टिपरं मनः।
दोषो ह्यविद्यमानोऽपि नाद्रिचात्रां प्रकाशते॥

Contents

Essays

Photographs

introduction

युवा वृद्धोऽतिवृद्धो वा व्याधितो दुर्बलोऽपि वा।
अभ्यासात्सिद्धिमाप्नोति सर्वयोगेष्वतन्द्रितः॥

"Young, old, excessively aged, diseased and even weak —
From mindful practice, all these can reach perfection in all practices of yoga."

Hathapradipika 1:64

ANYONE WHO HAS IMMERSED HIMSELF OR HERSELF IN THE PRACTICE OF YOGA, coming into contact with the plethora of yoga claims and advertising out in the world today, must question exactly what they are doing. When Dattatreya and I first came out of India and began teaching in Amsterdam, we went around looking at the advertising and the demonstrations. Then we wondered what we were doing. We saw advertisements for aqua yoga, spiritual strip tease, rebirthing in black and white or colour depending on the price and so on. We looked at the popular yoga literature and wondered even more what we were doing. Whatever yoga we were doing did not seem to have any relation to what was passing under the name of yoga. We found it humorous when an acclaimed international yoga teacher, one of the "yoga royalty," with a temple slide as background, in a dim mystic light in the Cosmos, threw her hands in the air and screamed "the mind is a hawk."

Yoga today is more popular than it has ever been. It has passed into the daily lingo of virtually every culture and country throughout the world. Most recently yoga was used in a rock show performed in sexy lingerie amidst the deafening thunder of relentless amplification that must have been like god speaking. It is, indeed, a new world order.

Originally yoga was practiced and passed on by people who had abandoned social structures and, from the point of view of society and culture, were outlaws on the fringe of socialization. Even today, serious practitioners of yoga, are still "left out" — but in a different way than before. Or perhaps, one could say, euphemistically, that they have retreated into a more personal space than that offered to us by contemporary culture.

1

If the academic and philosophical history of yoga is examined carefully, it is wanting. There are three major appropriation-manipulations in the history of yoga and a third minor one. First of all, there is a major political manipulation in the appropriation of Buddhist practices in the development of meditation and metaphysics. Then, in the second instant, the tenuous yoga-samkhya philosophical school was beleaguered by the vedanta school that was heavily indebted to a different stage of Buddhism. Vedanta, or more specifically, Sankara's version of advaita vedanta, eliminated the realistic dualism in favour of idealism. Vedanta, as yoga had previously, appropriated Buddhist techniques and turns of thought for its ultimate solution. Finally, there is political manipulation, which might be connected with some form of social morality, in the shift from a tantric viewpoint to a philosophical school. This must have occurred over a long period of time, but the final solution was accomplished by the categorical imperative in the time of the Vijayanagara kingdom and the *Sarvadarsanasangraha*, with its orthodox classification system. These historical political manoeuvres have left 'yoga theory' with a philosophical inconsistency. The rationality behind the Samkhya duality has been fatally destroyed.

Most of the hathayoga traditions claim some sort of alliance with the nathayoga movement. This claim derives from the *Hathapradipika* and other texts and is, suspiciously in some cases, an academic claim. The natha movement was one of those magical movements that left legend and nostalgia behind it. It was also influenced by the devotional movement and incorporated that as part of its popularization. Contemporary yoga movements have virtually no connection with the natha movement which has, on one side, lost its connection to yoga by becoming a social caste and, on the other, the ascetic side, been somewhat overwhelmed by its loss of societal status and failure to attract skill and learning.

The Dikshitars, Cidambaram temple custodians, represented a tantric yoga meditation school that they brought to Cidambaram from Kashmir. From 1608 to 1678, the temple was in the possession of the muslims and later, in the 1700's it was in the possession of the French as a fort, then the English and the Muslims again. The Dikshitars, who fled to Tiruvarur, lost their sadhana teachings with the temple and were never able to restore them. The formation of the dancing Siva at that temple was a very successful attempt to form a visual image of the principles of their metaphysics for a devotional tradition. That alone has survived. A Patanjali, not the renowned Patanjali, was an important teacher, indeed, perhaps the preceptor of their sadhana, in the Kashmiri Saiva tradition. This is the only temple where a Patanjali representation exists. (*Chidambaram and Nataraja* by B.G.L Swamy).

Under the British period, yogis were considered degenerates and freak performers, fakirs. Yoga subsequently came to be associated with illicit drugs and sex. Indeed, this reputation may have started well back into the natha period and was brought up almost to the present by the British with their

Victorian morality. Contemporary times have given yoga a new image of health, therapeutics and, curiously, retained the morality.

The most important historians of the yoga tradition at the beginning of this century have been the participants in the Lonavla Yoga School. Swami Kuvalayananda, the founder of that school, tested the claims of yoga phenomena; he documented his experiments, taught yoga, collected basic texts, edited them critically, and ran a yoga hospital. The contribution and influence of the Lonavla School, though somewhat neglected today, is remarkable. This period in India, near to independence, set in motion a striving towards establishing yoga as a legitimate, beneficial and admirable activity. There was a reclamation of culture. As with Indian dance, there was a necessity to reform yoga's image. The Lonavla School and the Maharaja of Mysore, through his patronized and guided teachers, were the prime motivators of this striving. They changed yoga from being a solitary and isolated activity, from being a curiosity and scorned activity under the British, to being a mainstream health activity, through its exercises and therapeutic capabilities, accessible to ordinary people all over the world.

There were many individuals who figured somehow in the history of yoga but their traces and effects are so minimal that it is difficult to trace them. It is not that they have not been important but that their importance has been on a limited number of individuals. This might be more important for the transmission of the benefits of yoga than the mass movements. It is a tradition of healers and teachers that have all but disappeared under chronic institutionalization. But they end up invisible, that is, "left out."

The yoga that is taught around the world today is a revivalist movement. I have traced that recent history of the revival in the book *The Yoga Tradition of the Mysore Palace*. This yoga tradition has strengthened itself from many sources — the ancient Indian wrestling tradition, western gymnastics, and the yoga tradition as it was in the early part of the last century in India. If the early yoga tradition drew on philosophical elements from diverse places, the recent yoga tradition has drawn on bodywork practices from diverse traditions.

The revival has brought new considerations to yoga — the legacy of functional anatomy of the physiotherapy schools (which is based on static bodies), therapeutic interest from a sustained interest in alternative medicine and lifestyle, and an exploration based primarily on external movement (as opposed to meditation). Indeed, movement seems to be the popular object of meditation rather than the mind or the breath. Movement can be a worthy meditation support as it involves feelings, sensations, thinking, surrender, renunciation and ultimately leads to the breath and the mind if thoroughly explored. Academic research into the history of yoga and scientific research into yogic phenomena and therapeutics is inadequate.

Yoga does have a unique position. It is the only exercise system based on stretching. All other exercise systems are based on contraction of muscle, aerobics, and have their origin in militaristic necessities of extending a weapon beyond the limits of the body.

The true historians of the yoga tradition have been the participants themselves. Most participants have left no records or sparse records of their journey with the exception of Theos Bernhard and Malladihalli who left extraordinary records. Because of the very nature of the yoga discipline, and because of its image in society, very few records have been left. It has not lent itself to commodification easily until the present. Often a publication on poor paper, of a very limited print run, is the only record of any activity. But the history of yoga is carried in the bodies of its practitioners for better or for worse.

B.K.S. Iyengar has been practically the sole communicator of the contemporary yoga tradition. His practices, his teaching and his publications have set the standards and brought yoga to a phenomenal number of people around the world. In this year, the Iyengar Yoga Teacher's directory on the web lists teachers in 42 countries. His book, *Light on Yoga*, has just sold over a million copies (communicated by Rajvi Mehta by email), indicating that his students number in the millions around the world.

The practice of yoga can be assessed from its direct benefits. It is, first of all, a source of well being of immense value in our current sedentary age. It removes stress, it gives an inner mobility to people literally hindered by age and sedentary lifestyles, it gives health and stimulus to the vital bodily organs. It keeps the mind in a state of creativity and well-being preventing depressions and illnesses of the mind. More than this, yoga is a spiritual discipline. It allows people to have an experience of something beyond their own limitations. And the experience is body-based meaning it is directly perceptible. It awakens them to something larger than themselves and provides them the means to sustain an attachment to something larger than themselves. The proof is in the practice. The taste of the cake that looks good in the window is only truly assessed by eating. It can look good and stimulate desire but it may not taste good and satisfy desire. It is, too often, merely sugar and rancid fat. Taste can be deceived too, of course. This is a world of deceit, a world that admires and worships deceit. Our very basic social organization hierarchy is somehow the source of that deceit and we remain attracted to and immersed in it. With that as backdrop, one can understand that yoga can be a means of ascertaining a form of truth that is directly relevant to one's body and soul. This may not be so for everyone — after all yoga has its fashions, its advertisements, its excesses and so on, but for the keen student of yoga, there is the realization that yoga is truth.

On Patanjali

WHEN CONSIDERING HOW TO BEGIN A DISCUSSION OF THE SUBJECT OF PATANJALI, a number of possibilities are apparent. I shall outline some of the more plausible approaches and, in some cases, evaluate them according to different points of view.

First of all, he is accepted as the author of the *Yogasutram* commonly dated to the second century BC. He is also supposed to be the author of a lost book on medicine and the *Mahabhasyam* on Panini's grammar. According to legend, as an incarnation of Adisesa, the cosmic serpent, he fell (*pata*) into the praying hands (*anjali*) of Gonika, as a tiny serpent that became a man.

It is almost certain that the author of the *Yogasutram* and the *Mahabhasyam* are different. These works are vastly different in terms of language, consistency and purpose. All of the other mythological/historical information on Patanjali is strictly legend. The legend of his mystical birth parallels the etymological breakdown of his name. It is a sobriquet.

The popularization of his name has come from his being designated the author of the *Yogasutram*, the oldest text that deals exclusively with yoga (there are older Upanishad texts that deal with yoga), and the academic enterprise around that text. Recently, I did a search for the name Patanjali on the internet search engine Google. It churned up 69 pages of approximately 15 entries per page. None of the basic academic reference material was mentioned. He was discussed in only two sites. Most of the sites related to some form of advertising, appropriating some kind of authenticity from the mention of the name Patanjali. Patanjali has become a magically potent celebrity name.

There was a Patanjali from Kashmir who may have migrated with Kashmir Saivite Yogins who founded the Cidambaram temple. There is evidence of him there as an acarya. The Dikshitar custodians of the temple practiced a particular meditation or vidya, a meditation on the space within the heart, that came to an end with the Muslim invasion when they fled to Tiruvarur. They were never able to revive the tradition again. This is the only temple in which there is a representation of Patanjali. It is not in the garbhagrha but on the carapace. The Nataraja of the temple is a visual icon based on the philosophical teaching created to provide a devotional image that has become popular. The idea of dance has connections to a cosmic legend of Patanjali's incarnation, and is thus, in a larger mythological sense, intriguing.

As the author of the *Yogasutram*, there are a number of observances that can be made. Patanjali's work has been the subject of Indian scholastic effort. The first commentary on the *Yogasutram* is by

Vyasa. It is commonly said that the *Yogasutram* would be virtually ununderstandable without this commentary. This commentary treats the *Yogasutram* as a whole, as a philosophical system. The later commentaries treat the *Yogasutram* as interpreted or explicated by that commentary. Nothing is known of this particular Vyasa, the author of that commentary.

The aim of a commentator on Indian philosophical texts was not to criticize that work. The aim was to explicate the implications of the work and ensure that the work was consistent philosophically. By that approach, a continuity of scholastic effort strove towards a single goal, the substantiation of the particular metaphysical presuppositions that the work supported. It is interesting to compare projects like the Kailasanatha temple at Ellora which was carried out by 7,000 artists over three generations to produce a unified whole, the excavation of the Kailasanatha temple from a rock mountain. Often commentators would abandon their own name to work under another well-known name in the hope that their commentaries would attract notice. This points, not to a critical collapse, but to a total abandonment of ego, a surrender of individuality to the larger metaphysic involved. While criticism has its place, it tends to look egomaniacal and trivial beside such enterprise.

In respect of yoga and teachers, such an attitude makes it possible to learn even from a bad teacher. Either way, it's all the same — if one carries things through to the end. That is the main thing.

The Threads of Yoga

"Seeing is divine."

LUDWIG FEUERBACH

The word "aesthetics" is derived from the Greek *aisthesis* meaning "perception."

तदेवार्थमात्रनिर्भासं स्वरूपशून्यमिवसमाधिः।

"Samadhi is when you see only that object, (the mind) being as if it were empty."

Yogasutram

A T ITS MOST BASIC LEVEL, the message of the *Yogasutram*, and all metaphysical knowledge disciplines, is that what we know, our memory, affects our perception. The Buddhists carried this to more extreme conclusions; they said that we see for a brief moment only. Then in the instant that we know what we see, we see the category imprints that are stored in our mind and no longer "see" as such. What we know of the world is our own conceptions, a mere fantasy, a dream, a figment of the mind, categories to live by. The aim of the disciplines outlined in the *Yogasutram* is directed towards purging the mind of the kind of memories that cause us to see incorrectly. That is why the sutra, defining samadhi, adds the words, *svarupansunyamiva*, literally "(the mind, *cittam*) empty as it were of its very nature." The mind is a repository of memory; it is the hard disk. It is never empty; it cannot be erased. Thus, the word *iva*, meaning "as if" is added to the sutra. There are abstruse commentaries on this sutra that I want to acknowledge but not elaborate, for the sake of simplicity.

This is part of Indian thinking. For example, in the *Mahabharata*, in the archery contest, various archers are asked to describe a bird target. They describe it in various ways. When Arjuna's time comes he says that he sees only the eye of the bird.

What can we really know of the *Yogasutram*? This text was written over two thousand years ago, is translated into countless languages, and has made its way into country after country from ancient China to modern America. Its author is referred to over 1000 times in websites, and is as much of a household word today as Mr. Clean. Now, consider carefully who has done this and how his name has been used.

The text is written in what is called the sutra, literally, the "string" style. The sutra, like the string, has been for various cultures like the Inca, a mnemonic device related to counting. The advent of the sutra style comes from a period in Indian thought when there was a necessity to consolidate knowledge. There were no books and no writing. The sutra style arose from the attempt to create a practical means for remembering complex rituals. Already for a thousand years, after the codification of the Vedas, oral memorization with checks was in practice and continued right down to our day. It was used to memorize the books of the Vedas, the grammatical texts and other disciplines as well. In the case of the *Yogasutram*, one might expect that the student would learn the text by heart and then go and put it into practice as part of his sadhana. All Indian metaphysical systems were meant to be put into practice; they transcended theoretical academics. Theoretical academics provided a framework, a teaching tool and were not expected to give more than general knowledge. The sutras, by this time, were a mnemonic device meant to provide a skeletal general view of the whole of an oral tradition. Without instruction in that oral tradition, it was impossible to understand their meaning couched in that abbreviated style. The oral instruction, the understanding of these was meant to relate to specifics rather than generalities. In the case of grammar and logic, meaning was conveyed by a careful precise metalanguage, a technical reference system defined by the sutras themselves.

There is a difference in approach to learning when one acquires a view of the whole and works on various steps for the consecutive realization of that knowledge. It differs from the cumulative approach where things are collected and stored without having a sense of the whole. The latter is a situation where someone gets an idea and then looks around for support for that idea. In scholarship this used to be the subject of scorn whereas now, it is an accepted methodology in scholarship. The undesirable contingency is that you promote yourself; you do not subsume yourself in your subject. Indeed, you have vested interests in promoting yourself; you become an intellectual ad agency. There are implications in this approach that question the validity of knowledge, the morality of knowledge, personal integrity, and the irrevocable links with acquisition in all aspects from primitive collection to fashionable modern greed. The cumulative approach belongs to cultures that insist on distraction as a means of social control. It creates things like computers that work under the impression that rapid classification of information is knowledge.

The sutras provided a personally accessible and immediate schemata of the whole, the parts of which could be worked on and realized individually, specifically and gradually.

These differences of approach have been commented on in the Upanisads themselves under the critique of the Aindra grammar. The Aindra grammar approached language by trying to collect and classify all the words of the language. It was rejected finally because words have no end. This was a means of learning previously in the west; people memorized dictionaries to know a language. It was not very successful considering that language is communication as opposed to accumulation. The Latin grammar and its superimposition on derivative languages is an example of such collection by categories and gave way to structural and generative grammars after an insight from observing Panini's grammar from 600 BC.

There are peculiarities within the sutras themselves. First of all, the yoga sutras are not in a true sutra style. When we compare the Paninian sutras on grammar and those on ritual, the *Yogasutram* is written in a rather careless manner. The sutras on grammar make specific reference; they work out a referent and abbreviation system that makes them internally consistent. This is not the case with the *Yogasutram*. While they are abbreviated, impossible to configure without some background, they are not written as a closed technical treatise. I have written papers on some of the specific problems in the sutras (*Journal of the Asiatic Society of Bombay*, Vol 70, 1995 & Vol 72, 1997).

In addition to this absence of a technical style, the *Yogasutram* contains terminology that has been borrowed from Jaina and Buddhist sources. For example, the term *kaivalya*, stated as the aim of the discipline, was a Jaina term. Other terms are pointed out in the above noted papers.

Secondly, there is no record of an oral tradition or practice tradition. I have discussed this problem in *The Yoga Tradition of the Mysore Palace*. There are countless references to yoga in nearly all the sastric works, there are references in the purana literature and in the upanishadic literature. There are textual indications of a practice tradition that dates back a 1000 years or more. But nowhere are there any indications of a yoga tradition connected with the *Yogasutram*. In fact, when one adopts a historical viewpoint that includes the practice tradition, there are substantial reasons for separating the yoga practice tradition from the academic tradition that has come down from the sutras. If one were to adopt a philosophical point of view, then there is further reason for a separation of the academic and practice tradition since the samkhya-yoga dualistic philosophical system was virtually eclipsed by Sankara and became a historical artifact after that. It does not appear that the samkhya tradition that was eclipsed had any close connection to the yoga academic tradition and Sankara, while barely mentioning it, goes on to state that yoga is satisfactory as a means but its metaphysics are to be disregarded. This is generous indeed, and would be totally unexpected if the yoga school presented any worthwhile challenge to his incisive thought.

The Indian schoolmen, looking at western philosophers, claim that western thinkers are unaware of their presuppositions. The doubt that provokes this observation is the understanding that, with logic, rationality or whatever else you need, you can support or even prove anything. Logic, being deductive (Indian logic does incorporate induction) cannot bring new knowledge; it can only establish soundly what is already stated and known in the premise. Therefore, it is essential to know exactly what the ultimate entities in the particular knowledge system are. "Realize" means perceiving directly; and refers to the specific perception of something that is beyond the realm of ordinary perception. It means that the system is validated by realization; not by elimination or epistemology or reason. If this were not the case, the knowledge would remain as a general knowledge rather than specific knowledge and thus be open to doubt.

On that topic, the Indian schoolmen believed that knowledge derived from inference or logic was a general knowledge and knowledge that is taught or comes by word of mouth, such as teaching and gossip, is also general knowledge. Thus, ultimately, that comes to be considered social or cultural knowledge. Without the specific direct perception, knowledge can be subjected to doubt and is thus, not helpful for forming any conclusion. It speaks *about* things rather than the things themselves. General knowledge can be helpful in warding off doubts that assail direct perception but it is not helpful finally. The direct perception of ultimate entities can be subject to doubt because it is not something verifiable by the physical eye.

The Indian system strove for and trained the student in concentration. It always took him inward. Terminology indicating that developed; terms like *ekagrata*, one-pointedness and so on because realization of these supersensuous entities was only possible through sustained concentration and attention without distraction or doubt. That is, realization required a mind/body capable of sustaining it.

Our ways of thought are oriented towards material reality. We are populating the world right in our languages with masses of objects. We speak of an information glut. We are in continual need of distraction and, in fact, seem to be seeking perpetual distraction. In fact, we consider our knowledge acquisition to be quantitative accumulation and our entertainment to be distractive dissipation. We are seduced into the mystery of distraction by our political ethics and by advertising. It is a means of control. But there are mysteries in concentration that are both mental and body practices. Yoga is the most refined approach to a concentration discipline ever developed and it has been refined over thousands of years. It is a unified mind/body approach. It is something that can be applied everywhere. What can a mind, fed on a gluttonous feast of distraction as culture, understand of a system that teaches the contrary? Is it going to learn something from that system or is such a mind going to transform that system into something more akin to its own agendas and simply return to business as usual? That is, make it another acquisition to be decorated, dusted off and trotted out for cocktail parties and then offered for sale without return. It is difficult to forget that the mind sees through its filters.

What, then, can we, with our baggage loading our perceptive abilities, understand of the *Yogasutram* and the metaphysical knowledge system outlined there that is, perversely, asking us to abandon our memory baggage that is so necessary for us to establish our individuality? What are the metaphysical presuppositions that we hold, that are known not by our declamation, but by the way we live, speak and move? What are the metaphysical presuppositions that are at the forefront of the *Yogasutram* and what relation do they have to our practice, our learning of yoga? What can we know of the *Yogasutram* from the text and the traditions prevalent at that time or later?

First we can talk about language. Sanskrit is an extremely difficult language to master. The language was originally rich in verb forms. The ancient Indians saw the world in terms of moving patterns of energy. This was reflected in the rich verbal forms — as many as 3,600 possible forms for each verb in Vedic Sanskrit. Nouns were flexible names — not names of things but names that varied in accordance to what percentage and nature of a particular verbal energy they were able to absorb at a particular moment. Thus there was a fluidity in the objects around us. Our languages, and Sanskrit as well, are tending towards nominalization. The failure of accumulative nominalization is already posed in the Upanisads in respect of the Aindra grammar mentioned earlier.

Over and above that, Sanskrit is a highly technical language. Nearly all of the phenomena described in metaphysical works are technical terms that have no correspondence in English. For example, take the word samadhi. The word samadhi has been popularized as some transcendent mystical state. How many people who use the word samadhi in English, use it in the sense defined in the *Yogasutram*? And after that, how many people are able to explain the sense of the definition in the *Yogasutram*? Nor can it be left at that because there are many qualifications of the definition given in the *Yogasutram*. There are many other words that are said to mean samadhi that are taken from different meditation disciplines like Buddhism. Further, each spiritual discipline would find it incumbent to define samadhi, in its own way.

But the word samadhi is explained very clearly in the *Yogasutram*. It means, as stated above, seeing things exactly as they are without any colouring by the mind. The word itself, etymologically, means something like *dha* "placing" (the mind) *a* "on" (something) *sam* (together or completely or correctly). In fact, the word comes to mean something like the hippy terminology used to describe someone, namely "together." When someone was "together" it meant that they saw things as they were, correctly, implying that the knowledge was somehow transcendent of their visual apparatus and related to their personal intelligence or something such. "Together" was almost a magic word. It has a ring similar to the coda *svarupasunyam*, the (mind) nature, as if, *iva*, empty. "Seeing it as it is" and "saying it like it is" were radical expression in the sixties in North America.

The metaphysical presuppositions, the ultimate entities of the different systems are clear in Indian thought. They are directly stated and can be easily reviewed.

Yoga is supposed to be a heritage of a dualistic system. It substantiates *purusa* and *prakrti*. These terms are given the designation spirit and matter. But they immediately conjure up their own baggage. *Purusa* literally means the male and *prakrti* means nature or natural, and comes to mean the female, or at least is taken that way.

These are the irreducible entities of the dualistic system. *Purusa* is the unengaged spirit entity that watches over the continuous fluctuations of *prakrti*. *Prakrti* is matter in various forms from this world right up to our own selves and our mind that is only active because *purusa* is in it. She is everything.

The problem that the Indian schoolmen had was with the connection between the two. This is the connection between spirit and matter, subject and object. Sankara begins the *Brahmasutram* by showing that there can be no possible connection between these two. The samkhya-yoga school has never been able to determine the relation satisfactorily and was, because of this very problem, eclipsed by Sankara's idealistic vedanta almost 1,500 years ago.

Indeed, there are seeds of vedanta right in the yoga-system. First of all, ultimate realization is regarded as the realization as isolation of *purusa*. *Prakrti*, having come to a state of stasis, existing only for the sake of *purusa*, serving as the medium for his realization of his own self, simply dwindles away to nothing, disappears, leaving pure *purusa*. This is strikingly similar to vedantic ideas of liberation and dubiously non-dualistic. In vedanta, the world, (*prakrti*), also the mind, when she becomes pure enough, like a magnifying glass, allows the light of the soul to shine through thus causing that mind to melt or disappear, as the magnifying class causes the rays of light to kindle fire thus burning the dross around, leaving pure unadulterated spirit. The realization is that the world is illusion, unreal. And the subject has become a real man. And he propagates too. There is a world full of *purusas* out there.

Secondly, though determined before the gender wars, we are suspicious of the historical legacy of male-female connection and separation in the terminology. In fact, I personally think that the yoga-samkhya school as it has been handed down was an outgrowth of the tantric schools where conjugation between male and female was considered to be the microcosm of the origin of the universe. As it became orthodox philosophy, conjugation became fornication with all its discontents and had to be clothed in more appropriate drag. There is nothing like a name change to make a product fly. Chinese gooseberries were a marketing disaster until they became kiwi fruits. *Purusa* and *prakrti* were just sufficiently decent to fly as philosophy. It was just the connection.

Thirdly, I think that original samkhya looked very different from what is known of it today. The word *samkhya* means number. It has a suggestion of counting. The early schools of Buddhism, where samkhya grew, were counters. They enumerated the characteristics that all materia and phenomena consisted of. They were determining what the basic entities were, logically — what things consisted of. They were trying to trace things back to their real origins in the face of change. There is a connection between these practices and samkhya. I have elaborated this in a previous referred to paper. In fact, Gautama Buddha's first teachers were samkhya philosophers. They drew on the same teachings and found different things at the end of materia. The legacies of counting still exist in yoga.

Thus the connection to Buddhist thought in the *Yogasutram* is entirely expected and anticipates the need to distinguish the yoga school from that. Hindus did revolt against Buddhists and their learning and the revolt is recorded in the history of the logic, the vedantic and the yoga schools of thought. In fact one can distinguish exactly which particular schools of thought in Buddhism they were revolting against. It is not possible to understand the Hindu schools of thought without understanding the Buddhist points that they are trying to refute or appropriate as the case may be, even though they are bloodied over.

And there are still further things to account for if we want to understand the *Yogasutram* meaningfully. Although the Indian commentators after Vyasa have commented on the text as if it were a philosophical whole, there are many doubts about that. Some say that the text is a composite, a compendium of different elements of spiritual disciplines that are merely put together and given some kind of order — that the text has no consistency as a whole unit.

The arguments for the text as a whole unit should speak for themselves. Apart from the early commentators, the most recent authentic spokesman for that is Swami Hariharananda Aranya. He was trained as a pandit or sastri and wanted to realize the teachings. After prolonged study, he spent years living in seclusion. He wrote a commentary on the text which, in my opinion, is the most meaningful commentary written. Still, like his predecessors, his intention was to make the original meaningful. Criticism is considered, in these traditional schools, to be an indication of personal failure as well as an ethical breach. Everything is what you make it. Consider the previous qualifications of realization. His devotion did not quite make the text speak clearly.

On the composite text side, there is a host of linguistic evidence that points to multiple sources. The word *kaivalya* and other words as well come from Jainism. Many words and concepts come from Buddhism. There is a lack of internal consistency in the text in terminology that indicates grafting of concepts. In general, one can cite the popular Indian tendency to synthesize, a survival from the metaphysical schools of thought now in disarray.

With these considerations, how should a modern student of yoga approach the primary text? As stated, earlier, the text has been made prime use of by cherry pickers. They have been picking up a slogan here and a slogan there for the sake of advertising or for establishing their authenticity. There are things that can be made use of in the text, that have profound implications. There are astounding insights. But they have to stand in their own right. They cannot be supported within the whole context of the text. This is the situation that a serious student of yoga, wishing to immerse himself in what are considered authentic originating teachings, has to deal with.

In the context of the other schools of thought, the *Yogasutram* appears to be superceded. There are schools that say that Buddhism is the logical outcome of the logical materialist schools. Indeed, the logicians were called nihilists by their contemporaries. And vedanta is the logical outcome of the dualistic samkhya school. They were also considered nihilists. Both of the earlier schools had reached a philosophical impasse. In order to resolve this philosophical dilemma, vedanta declared the world unreal, brahman real. Buddhism declared the world ultimately real, spiritual entities unreal. They both had to posit illusion or unreality to establish their idealistic schools on sound philosophical principles. Never mind that this is a terrifying concession at the level of ultimate entities. Vedanta's revival was really the result of a borrowing from Buddhism and a wave of popularity. The logical schools had a brief revival but it was not accessible to ordinary people. Contemporary study of vedanta is not about vedanta but devotion to vedanta. The cherry pickers are busy there too. It is the popular wave of yoga, brought on by the great teachers that originated with the Mysore Palace that have brought the cherry pickers to the yoga sutras again. It is cherry blossom time.

राजयोगः समाधिश्च उन्मनी च मनोमनी ।
अमरत्वं लयस्तत्त्वं शून्याशून्यं परं पदम् ॥
अमनस्कं तथाद्वैतं निरालम्बं निरञ्जनम् ।
जीवन्मुक्तिश्च सहजा तुर्या चेत्येकवाचकाः ॥

"Rajayoga, Samadhi, Unmani (beyond the mind), Manomani (jewel of the mind), Amaratvam (immortalness), Laya (dissolved), Tattva (reality), Sunyasunya (absolutely empty), Parampada (the supreme goal), Amanaska (mindlessness), Advaita (non-duality), Niralamba (without support), Niranjana (without colour), Jivanmukta (released while living), Sahaja (the natural state), Turya (the fourth state) — all of these describe the same thing."

Hathapradipika 4.4

NB: These are all different words used to describe the goals of various spiritual disciplines. Thus the translations are only to give a sense of the words. Svatmarama, the author of the *Hathapradipika*, enumerates a number of them and states that they are all the same. Revelation is revelation no matter what form it is in.

अथ यदा सुषुप्तो भवति। यदा नकस्य चन वेद ।
हिता नाम नाड्यो द्वासप्ततिः सहस्राणि हृदयात्
पुरीततमभिप्रतिष्ठन्ते । ताभिः प्रत्यवसृप्य पुरीतति शेते ॥

स यथोर्णनाभिस्तन्तुनो ॽरेद्यथाऽग्नेः क्षुद्रा
विस्फुलिङ्गा व्युच्चरन्त्येवास्मादात्मनः सर्वे प्राणाः
सर्वे लोकाः सर्वे देवाः सर्वाणि भूतानि व्युच्चरन्ति।
तस्योपनिषत् सत्यस्य सत्यमिति । प्राणा वै सत्यं तेषामेष
सत्यम् ॥२.१.१९,२०॥

"Now when one goes into a deep sleep, when one knows nothing whatsoever, having crept out through the 72,000 *nadis* called *hitas* that lead from the heart (the mind) to the surrounding body, he rests in that body. And having returned by those (*nadis*), he rests in the heart (mind).

As a spider comes out on a thread of web, as tiny sparks from a fire, just so, from this self, come all the *pranas*, all worlds, all gods, all creatures. This *upanisad* speaks the reality of what is. The *pranas* are the reality. This soul is their reality."

Brhadaranyakopanisad 2.1.19 & 20

nadis

OGA HAS ASTOUNDING AFFECTS ON PEOPLES' HEALTH AND WELL BEING whether followed as a spiritual discipline or merely practiced as a mild form of exercise.

Of our own non-drug oriented health systems or traditions, it is perhaps chiropractory and homeopathy that have had the most sustained and beneficial results. D.D. Palmer, a magnetic healer, began with manipulations of the spine. His effectiveness came from an understanding of Oriental medicine meridians and the stimulation of them. The meridians are clarified mostly in Chinese and Japanese medicine systems. There was a sustained period of body knowledge and medical interchange with the spread of Buddhism and the martial arts from India. The forefront of the Indian cultural spread was ayurvedic medicine — literally, the understanding of life.

The revitalization of chiropractory in our time has come again from kinesiology, a re-orienting to the meridian complexes of Chinese medicine. This diagnoses from weaknesses in the muscle relating that to weaknesses in specific organs and then to imbalances in the energy flows. Chiropractory then, diagnosing from the physical structure and manipulating it, influences the energy pulses running in the body to determine, affect and rectify imbalances in the vital forces.

In Chinese and Japanese medicine, specific points are stimulated by means of needles, acupressure, heat and various other types of stimulation where the energy flow is hindered or blocked. This can also be done by bringing up the pulse over that area, by stimulating or attracting the flow of energy in the *nadi*, the vessel or path of the vital force. In accompanying treatment complexes, organs and life forces are stimulated by means of herbs.

The meridian lines and the theory of pulses have probably come from Indian medicine. There was a period, totally neglected historically, where Indian medicine spread around the known world (in distinction to the western propagation of weapons and economic savagery). Indian documentation of the pulses in the body dates back to the Upanisads, some of which date back to 1,500 BC. The atma-prana theory and the five element theory can be found in even earlier texts. Even today, skilled Ayur Veda practitioners can diagnose on the basis of the energy pulses running in the body and prescribe nutritional supplements that bring the body into balance. There are traces of a system of *marmas* or vital points that were used for stimulation, manipulation and destruction. These were passed on with Buddhist monks, some yogic texts and the martial art schools like *kalaripayattu* which reached different levels of refinement in schools in Japan and China in the monasteries. The idea of the *qi*, a concept in many ways like *prana* and pathways of that or the meridian lines, make their appearance in the *Huangdi Neijing* and in two earlier works, the *Zubi Shiyi Mai Juijing* and the *Yingyang Shiyi Mai Jiujing*. The Indian speculation appears equally early and is fully developed. Historical documentation is lacking.

The significance of this leads to a perception of the body, not as a body of discrete parts and even organs, but of a body formed by countless rivers of energy whose unimpeded and infinite flow was the source of well-being. This vision is embedded in language as mentioned before. It was the metaphysical presupposition that enabled perception of something that is immediately imperceptible.

Yoga made the most sustained and complex approach to the meridian lines. Rather than external stimulation, yoga, through physical balance and alignment opens the energy meridians throughout the body realigning muscular and organ structure, balancing the structural support, balancing the internal pressures in organs, implementing increased blood irrigation and then stretching the meridians such that it stimulates the energy flow through them. Stretching of the meridian, a clearing of the nadi, removes the blockages, literally knots (*granthas*) in yogic terminology, physically; from inside the body and realigns the energy patterns in terms of the whole body. This can only occur after cessation of muscular effort, accomplished by breath, when the body structure is in alignment and balance. This is a unique approach and contrasts to the physical, chemical and nutritional stimulation complexes that were the original and main line of development. The mechanistic reductionist symptom-obsessed model did not exist at this time. Without belittling the other approaches which all have their places, the yoga system was particularly effective since it did not depend on any external force, since it was effected from within and by the body and integrated directly with body, mind and spirit. It is fully co-ordinated. It is a realization of cessation from action rather than submission. It is a realization that the end of movement is stillness. Its results are directly and immediately tangible — only a worked muscle relaxes; an unworked muscle is merely dormant. Other approaches were able to work with more concentration on a particular spot but were seldom able to integrate it into the whole body system as successfully as yoga.

Yoga's approach emphasizes balance and alignment in the asana, since it is through that the meridian line is stretched or contracted, cleared and restored to unhindered energy flow. The energy flow was designated *saura*, literally connected with the sun-related sap flowing in plants. It is more important than the physiotherapeutic muscle-mechanics approach. It has been neglected since it was less accessible, less familiar, in western traditions. Even its appearance in chiropractory, magnetism and alternative medicines has been downplayed. The marketing techniques are different for things that have been left out of our brave and brazen culture. There are conflicts between the different approaches.

Headstand, for example, often considered the *raja*, literally the ruler or king of asanas, is physiologically contra-indicated because all the body weight is supposedly on the axial vertebra not designed to carry that weight. From other points of view, the headstand is a direct and total-body stimulation of the governor vessel. A sustained headstand is a reversal of all normal pressures on the organs and the spine and a gentle cleansing of venous blood by gravity. Its effect on the mind and the nervous system are distinctly and individually verifiable. Further, if done properly, the weight is not carried entirely on the axial vertebra but on the shoulders and forearms and with the body itself. It is of utmost value in correcting the numerous functional scolioses that do not respond to manipulation in other positions and have not been aided by medical interventions. The implications of this, in itself, are astounding. Its effects on stress are nothing short of miraculous. I could go on. But this is merely by way of example to indicate considerations that can be mustered against gross and inaccurate mechanistic materiality. Further, yoga teachers for years have said that you can be sued for teaching headstand — an economic weapon of illusion to top the list. But no one has been sued as far as I know. Granted, headstand, done improperly, can cause damage. The headstand can almost be considered the very mind of yoga. Breath would have to be its soul. There is no yoga without headstand.

The concept of stretching has recently been incorporated into physiotherapy practices in Holland and Sweden. It has placed them at the forefront of physiotherapeutic advancements. North America still remains foundered, for the most part, on repetitive machine mechanics. This again is the influence of monetary considerations overriding individual and healing relationships in favour of industrial cost-effective measures. It fails, as usual, to recognize the holistic aspect of healing which is necessary even in mechanical problems. The world is larger than machines and mechanics in spite of the continuing dream wars and machine love. Of course, the name yoga, the source of the most developed and complex stretching system is not acknowledged anywhere in the realms of professionalism and the physio systems in Holland and Sweden have incorporated stretching under different names than yoga.

I want to speak of another asana, *viparitacakrasana*. The backbend practice from Iyengar asks for 108 repetitions of this asana. This is a magic number in Indian tradition and, according to the nathas stood for the seven planets plus the waxing and waning of the moon making nine, through the twelve months of the year making 108. This backbend practice then is the cosmic year wheel turned backward.

Mechanically this is a backward flip with gymnastic origins. In gymnastics, it is accomplished with speed. In yoga it can be seen somewhat differently. First of all, in distinction to most asanas, it is a dynamic asana. There are asanas that come to a static conclusion and there are other asanas that are moving asanas. This, indeed should be the division of asanas. This asana is motion and co-ordination in motion. The asana requires a continual checking of speed and force in order to bring the asana into the spine, into the body away from the sense of accomplishment and the imbalance and loss of control when force is applied, when limb musculature is invoked. The movement progresses inward, away from the use of the limbs, which initiate force and speed, and becomes a movement centered in the spine. The asana requires a double movement of the spine. First the spine is bent backwards starting from the top of the back and then, after the inversion height is reached, a counter movement is initiated from the pelvis coming down the spine moving it in the opposite direction. It is difficult to initiate the counter movement. It is a movement that has to be initiated when the body can no longer initiate it easily from its preferred base on the floor. The tendency is to fall from the height since an internal, active and coordinated reversal of energy direction is required. It requires a switch within the brain through stillness, emptiness. This switch is a body knowledge; an intuitive body knowledge accomplishment. It requires a shift to a different area of the brain. A determined mind switch throws the co-ordination into disarray. A stretch of total body capability and then compression of the abdominal cavity organs and muscles is affected by dynamic mobilization that penetrates areas not amenable to a static stretch. This is evident to any practitioner of this asana. The asana requires the absolute attention and abeyance of the mind. You must hang on and let go. Mental intervention disrupts the body intelligence. The disruption is like static. The breath must be part of the whole co-ordination. The asana starts aerobically, physically. As dynamic balance is realized, the movement becomes an exercising, a circling of the vital energy, the submission of the self to the circular movement, a realization of the self, in total humility, as dynamically balanced in that body circle.

This asana, loaded with history and symbols, of suspect origin, of unfathomable therapeutic value may be at the heart of yoga as a process of rejuvenation and realization. It is a development of the headstand into an impelling dynamic. Its complexity of dynamic balance insists on a total inner balance, a total bodily harmony. It is the pin of the *Vijnana Bhairava*, the manual giving 112 means (*dharanas*) of attaining one-pointedness, that draws the mind inside when nothing else works.

Calacalam Asanam

AN ANCIENT DIVISION OF THE WORLD — in Indian thought — can be traced back right into the Vedas. The world is divided into still and moving things. The word static comes from the Sanskrit root *stha* which is also the source of words like estate, state, status, stature, statue and so on, giving an idea of how important this word is for our conceptual thinking — it touches on physical, psychological, social, political and metaphysical complexes.

The other term, the moving element, has particular significance for western people since it links with ideas of the dynamic, with ideas of progress that are a Christian and capitalist imperative so permeated into our psyche that we cannot think without that concept. It is part of our presupposition complex. On the Sanskrit side, an intensive of this word, *cal*, namely *cancalam* means fickle. Our ideas of dynamic, which have developed in the direction of constant distraction, are similar to that verbal root idea of fickle. Although we seldom consider it, there is a borderline between dynamic and fickle that is flexible; that is, dependent on our point of view.

Asanas can also be divided between still and moving asanas. It is a division that is eminently sensible and has implications for practice that we seldom consider. Of course the division is not absolute — nearly all asanas have to incorporate a degree of movement and all asanas must incorporate a degree of stillness. To classify in this way, one has to focus on the vital part of each particular asana. It means we have to pay attention to movement and its interplay with our balance, that is, our internal body movement. Movement is not mere mechanics — all of our past and our presence are touched by it.

Patanjali's sutra describing the means to accomplish an asana is: *prayatnasaithilyanantasama-pattibhyam*. I have discussed the meaning and significance of this sutram in my book *The Yoga Tradition of the Mysore Palace*. The meaning: "*the asana (is done) by slackening the effort and meditating on the endless.*" The sutra indicates that effort is necessary to perform the asana; that one must let go of this effort and attain to a total stillness (meditate on the endless). This is a significant statement. It tells us that each asana involves body mechanics, and at some point has to transcend body mechanics, right up to the very desire to move, in order to attain fullness, stillness.

Gert Van Leeuwen has particularized the meaning of this sutra by his creative work in yoga movement. He says that effort is under the control of the mind that controls the movement muscles. These movement muscles however override the deep structured postural muscles. In order to bring the postural muscles into play, the movement muscles have to release. The "slackening of the effort" correlates to this. Underlying this, the postural muscle engagement, is a sense of ease and balance since the postural muscles relate to our basic nature-structure. The movement muscles are not only under the control of the mind, but they are the repository of our past deeds and habits. They override the postural muscles and pull us, relentlessly and invisibly, out of balance. It is easier to hold on than to let go. We hold on with the movement muscles. While they function, nothing else can reveal itself.

The definition mentioned above is a functional definition. Patanjali defines asana as *sthirasukham*. With the above, we can interpret this apparently simple definition significantly now. *Sthira* means steady, strong and so on. *Sukham* means joyful or pleasant. The asana becomes *sthira* when we renounce the movement muscles in favour of the postural or basic structural muscles. When we engage with the movement muscles that are invoked from desire, intention; we pull ourselves out of balance in order to accelerate into a position. There is no steady balance in that. We renounce balance in favour of acceleration. When we have pulled ourselves out of balance, the asana is no longer pleasant. We have to exert ourselves further to maintain balance coming more and more under the scope of the movement muscles. Thus, we can understand the profundity of Patanjali's definition. He points the way to the transcendence of desire at a bodily level thus giving us a grass roots, a basic body knowledge means of working with the most obtuse power in our body. Further, he points the way to a satisfaction that is not a generated pleasure, but the deep pleasure of finding our basic self. We find this by "letting go." It is this shift in the brain that can give us a momentary mirror glimpse of ourselves.

In the *Mahabhasya*, Patanjali says that any word pronounced properly is enough to take you to heaven. This comes from ideas in the Vedas that a mantra, pronounced improperly, became impotent, even harmful. The idea was that, by going backwards on a word, into the mind, you reached the primal vibration or movement that was the desire to speak. It was this vibration that started the universe. Thus, through that sound, you can return to your origin, literally, your cosmic origin, the origin of life. These are some of the ideas behind ritualistic sacrifice. Transcendence is a sacrifice, a submission. In the flesh, in terms of movement, it means letting go of the movement muscles; it means allowing a different, older part of the brain to kick in.

And in terms of knowledge — what does it mean? The Indian schoolmen were not content to leave their knowledge as accumulation. They wanted their knowledge to transform them, civilize them. They wanted to move from the primitive accumulation oriented part of the brain into deeper parts where things came together. They could only reach these parts by letting go and ultimately, it meant letting go of everything. Civilization can only mean being able to include rather than to exclude. This is a form of undetermined synthesis that becomes all-inclusive. This is close to the root meaning of the word brahma. It means to expand, to open…and by extension, without limitation. This is Shankara's teaching.

What do we mean by visually by transcendence? Look at the pictures of the asanas in this book. They speak for themselves. They speak of a stillness beyond the movement muscles.

What is the purpose of dividing asanas into still and moving asanas? Of course, each asana configuration, when accomplished within the scope of body knowledge brings about an active development in the brain. Working within the scope of body knowledge means that every moment of body movement and stillness is absorbed fully, emotionally and intellectually, to the exclusion of other things, in the brain. It means that the asana is done with total commitment, attention, with the honesty we are capable of. This distinguishes itself from asanas that merely mimic a position and can be done, by determination, while answering the telephone and feeding the ferret. In other words, the asana is a fresh creation; it continues to be an exploration, meditation and revelation. The complexity of the energy patterns for each asana movement and the state of the body at each particular time, the complexity of the engagement of brain, nerves, muscles, sense of balance ensures that each asana is a new movement that ultimately reaches very old parts of the brain. However, repetitive-compulsive movement that lacks awareness can easily override that freshness of movement.

There are many static asanas. These are asanas, like the headstand, the standing asanas, forward bends to a large extent. There are asanas that are transitional like *sarvangasana* and twistings. These asanas require continual shifting of position, a constant striving for realizable space, as different muscle groups let go. They are asanas that we use specifically to penetrate further into the body. They appear static because we hold them for long periods of time to give an opportunity for the body to accommodate, to let go and move further. They are slow sustained stretches.

And there are asanas that are primarily dynamic like the balancings, like many of the advanced backbends and particularly, the most dynamic of all the asanas, *viparitacakrasana*. Balancings work somewhat differently. They start from movement, go through a more intense dynamic to reach stillness where bodyweight, in balance, challenging symmetry, is used for sustained penetration into the body. They too are a complex meditation.

The division of still and moving is a division in most cases, of degree. It is possible to note at this point that this is a division, like that between dynamic and fickleness, restlessness, or hyperactivity that occurs through our own determination, our commitment, our attention and our integrity. Asanas shift from being static to dynamic depending on what we put into them, what our degree of accomplishment is in that asana, and what our degree of attention is at each particular moment. The desire for accomplishment easily overrides attention.

Asanas are static for two reasons. One is that we have reached the end of movement in that asana and have transcended the desire to move. "Transcended," means having reached the end of movement;

it means having transcended the activities of the mind and body that focus on accomplishment as distinct from full balance. It is a surrender. It means that we have abandoned the memories in the body and attained a new fullness. In some cases we reach stillness because we are limited in that asana, are mimicking the form of the asana, and have simply given up, enduring a propped up position until the relief of cessation makes itself manifest. This distinguishes itself from the surrender of body and mind in the former instance. There is a tendency brought on by teaching outside of tradition, by the exigencies of the body, by the demands of accomplishment itself to look at the asanas as an approximation to some external form and to mimic that particular form. The failure to use the asana as a means of exploration of the energy patterns of the body is to use it as a prop. It might be helpful, temporarily, like all the other performance enhancing drugs.

Actually, there does not have to be any end of movement. One can continue adjusting and striving. Everything just keeps getting tighter and tighter. That is why surrender is necessary. Surrender or transcendence is the only way we can actually complete a movement, free ourselves from the obsession of achievement by the movement muscles.

A massive dogma of position has developed which points to an external linear path for attaining each asana. The insistence on the absolute objectiveness of each asana is a tendency of our age brought on by the idea that the asana is another product that can be produced by unleashing and worshipping the admen. But asanas are a mere tool to use to work on one's own limitations. There is no question of accomplishment; it is alien to the very idea of yoga where the direction is inward. The shift of the center of attention from the work of the asana and the qualification evaluating the asana by its adherence to a desired form is contrary to the spirit of yoga.

If skill in accomplishment were the purpose of yoga, it would not have been with us for the last few thousand years. An asana only has value where it is used to explore, to work on one's body. Consider that each single body is individual, that each time has its own pressures and trends, and that each start is a new world and it is easy to understand that there is no single asana or set of asanas that can provide a panacea for all bodies and times. Asanas change with the time, with the body. There is no formula or technique that can be taught in a lineal fashion that has as its aim mimicry of particular posturings that has any sense or meaning whatsoever. Note that the definition of asana given by Patanjali seizes on a vital description that could effectively cover any movement. Tradition must be dynamic in order to survive.

Traditional teaching is not object-oriented teaching. What it teaches is the means to correct knowledge. (See: The Memory Eye, *Journal of Indian Philosophy* 14, 1986). It is up to the student to verify, determine and use the teachings in their own way. It is an all-comprehensive teaching that covers body, mind, metaphysics and the ability to see into other bodies intuitively. Each asana is a meditation of varying complexity by which one can come to stillness. It is a pathway. Traditional teaching develops intuition. Yoga teaches many things. It reveals to us the ultimate worthlessness of determined effort in favour of intuition. It does not teach us the exercise of intuition but receptivity to intuition. You have to learn to wait.

Now there are asanas that are almost purely dynamic. I have discussed *viparitacakrasana* in the section on nadis. But let us look closer at this asana and what it demands of us in terms of dynamics.

Viparitacakrasana requires a consecutive opening of the spine, vertebra by vertebra in the backdrop. If a thought intervenes, if there is a momentary lack of awareness, or a concentration on accomplishment, and part of the spine does not open right where the thought occurred, then the flow of energy through the body is disrupted and one has to resort to speed, strength, or an extreme opening elsewhere to complete the movement. Sometimes, one is unable to tuck the hands in at the last moment and the chest does not activate making it necessary to use limbs to initiate the jump. Dancer's and gymnasts use speed and limbs but Yogis use the breath — they have an intuitive awareness of the unconscious movements of the body so that they can follow these internal movements through the body and let the very core of the body, the spinal column work for them. They have to find where the initial vibration for movement comes from. They have to let go of the conscious mind. They have to surrender to intuitive body awareness.

The most difficult movement in the *viparitacakrasana* is the reversal of the spine when the legs are straight up in the air in a single moment of stillness. It comes from turning in the thigh muscles and lengthening the sacrum. The initiation of a strong movement in the pelvis allows the legs to descend in control and affects an abandonment of the chest movement. It requires a transfer of mobilized centers. The spine remains awake. The movement remains cleanly in the pelvis allowing the mind to remain clear and alert, floating. When the spine bends, the mind collapses and the inevitability of gravity overwhelms the body like Newton's pain. Correct movement in this asana makes the spine sing.

Students of dance habitually use their limbs. Gymnasts use speed. The mind does not permeate the whole body in either of their movements. Dancers extend into a world beyond the limitations of their body; they flow outwards in spirals. Gymnasts deposit their family jewels in the energy of movement. But yoga goes inside, it seeks awareness of that movement, it goes inside and seeks the very soul of the movement, the desire to move and its purification in cessation, abandoning the usual invasive tools. Speech begins with the desire to speak. That desire is the primal vibration. Similarly, the desire to move as it unfolds completely in the body, is our most immediate universe, our first world.

Balancings are complex meditations. They are primarily a moving asana. They require movements of the body learned from static asanas. These attainments are taken off of their base and placed on our hands, the only contact with the floor that remains. That means that all of our body weight, all of the added stresses of a body configuration are deposited in various ways onto the hands on which balance is exorcised. They are a profound exploration of our sense of balance forcing it into different areas of the body asymmetrically by the configurations taken with the legs. The abandonment of symmetry in the configuration is a profound need. While stretching one side of the body, other parts must be totally relaxed. The moment of stillness is found only with constant practice and effort in balancings. Like an artist, if you want to be a yogin, you will have to suffer. That is the main thing. Balance is no easy thing. After attainment and balance, there is a slackening of the effort in specific parts of the body. It is an exercise in spaced brain alignment. The balance itself, confined to the fulcrum spot of balance and spread through the configuration is the stillness sought in these asanas. The balance is subordinate to the complex dynamics required for the asana, hence, the stillness is achieved only through a dynamic configuration and letting go within the puzzle of that configuration.

The word *jagat* in Sanskrit, meaning "world" is an intensive of the root *gam* which means "to go". The world is that which keeps going and going. In this way, we can understand the significance of asanas that start in some internal vibration, attain to a complex configuration that explores outwardly until they turn inwards again, return to rest, to stillness, not in external space but in the space within the heart. We can understand how each asana requires total attention, surrender, transcendence. We can understand each asana as an evolving and returning universe.

The division, still and moving asanas, as well as reflecting the nature of the world in a cosmic sense, reflects the vital essence of asanas. The word asana itself derives from the root *as* which means to sit, become still. It is a serious challenge in the ferocious battle against distraction.

Movement by Numbers

आचार्यः पादमादत्ते पादंस्वब्रह्मचारिभिः।
पादंस्वशिष्यमेध्या पादंकालक्रमेण च ॥

"The acarya (teacher) gives you one quarter, one quarter comes from your fellow students, one quarter comes from your own intelligence and one quarter comes from the passage of time."

MANU

"The execution of an action by no means proves that we know, even superficially, what we are doing or how we are doing it. If we attempt to carry out an action with awareness — that is, to follow it in detail — we soon discover that even the simplest and most common of actions, such as getting up from a chair, is a mystery, and that we have no idea at all how it is done."

MOSHE FELDENKRAIS, Awareness through Movement

ACCOMPLISHING MOVEMENT IN AN ASANA IS BEST ACHIEVED when a specific series of steps are followed.

First of all, manipulation or mobilization, an opening, can show your mind what can be done. It reveals a possibility or a possible direction. It is an external aid, a prompt to visioning, the initial "seeing" of a movement.

It is important, because we cannot work beyond the limits of our perception. It is impossible to access an area that is outside of the realms of perception. And the body contains "*granthas*" or knots that block perception. They block both mental (visualization possibilities) and bodily perception because it simply feels like that area is structurally impossible to access.

After manipulation, the most efficient way of accessing an area is through passive movement, accomplished by relaxation of tension belonging to the area and the tension that comes from effort. There are many movements in yoga that allow us to use body weight while coming out of, or going into an asana. If that body weight is used wisely, it can be used to penetrate those areas where there is a block on mental and bodily perception. It can be used to reveal and re-orient parts of the body that refuse access. This is a practice that has to be built up with skill and attention over a long period of time. It requires constant repetition with acute awareness. It requires absolute attention. There is nothing to "do" as such; it requires the development of awareness in these areas. Awareness is the single most important tool for initiating change.

One of the most obvious movements is the descent from *sarvangasana*. First of all, the arms must be placed over the head. If placed beside the body, they bear part of the weight of the body and thus obfuscate the reading from the spine. As the person descends from *sarvangasana*, he or she engages tight spots in his or her back that throw him or her off the center of the spine or spots that remain stiff and bypassed by the descent movement. The muscles in the shoulders and around the neck retract to protect areas of the spine, mostly, the lower back. Body weight, a pause in the movement to allow these tight areas to open, and breath are the tools to ascertain where tight areas are and to convince them to open.

When awareness is developed from the passive movement, active participation can begin. The transition has to be done with great care because active participation engages historical surface muscle patterns. First of all, the person can learn to open in the passive movement. Then they can begin to transpose that to the active element of the movement where body weight is carried by balance and breath. The process of taking over parts of the body with postural muscles is so slow that the person doing it usually does not even know it has happened. They see it in the results, of what they are "suddenly" able to do, of how they feel about themselves. Sometimes this can be shown with photographs. Often very dramatic results are unfelt — straightening of the spine, straightening of pelvic tilt and so on. Suddenly, they become normal. The are instantly assimilated because they, and not the hindrances, are actually one's self and one recognizes it.

Each of these accomplishments, aside from mobilizing blocked areas of physical structure, is an opening or revitalizing of an area of the brain. When awareness comes to a body complex, there is a corresponding expansion of the brain. And that, often linked with an emotional complex, can lead to the mediation of that particular emotional complex. Instead of a reality, there is awareness that the emotional complex is an illusion, a constructed reality. There is an inextricable connection between body and mind. The division is artificial.

Asanas are not meant to be objectified, polished and performed like athletic skills. They are meant to be used to work on your body, your mind. Each asana is a key to unlock something efficiently. Asanas are used to polish your mind so that light from the soul can pass through your body and mind and illuminate everything around you. When asanas are done correctly they are a revelation of the harmony of body, mind and spirit.

And if you know something of that, you need to share it. It is pointless and immoral to use it in any other way.

ईशावास्यमिदं सर्वं यत्किंच जगत्यां जगत्।
तेन त्यक्तेन भुञ्जीथा मा गृधः कस्य स्विद्धनम्॥

"This whole world stinks of God. Whatever moving thing there is in this moving world.
With that abandoned, enjoy. Do not be greedy for the riches of anyone at all."

Isopanisad

Hands On

MOVEMENT IN THE BODY IS A PSYCHOPHYSICAL EVENT. If the mind is carefully considered, there is a conscious element, the desire or decision to move, the autonomous balance complex, an unconscious co-ordination element, and execution of the movement by the movement muscles. When we decide to go and open the door, our body movement is on automatic, the autonomic nervous system takes care of it all. We have no conscious intervention beyond the decision. The decision itself invokes the particular movement muscles and takes care of the balance and muscle co-ordination.

If the complexity of a single movement is considered, then it could be visualized as a very large number of fluid electro-patterns running through the body. The dynamic nature, flexibility and complexity are staggering.

If one studies anatomy, one is overwhelmed first by the sheer number of muscles. If access is sought to each of these muscles, through palpation or massage, it adds a completely new level of thinking. This is a knowledge that has come from the examination of the dead, of cadavers. And then, if one wants to understand how the mechanics of each movement take place through muscle, bone and the clouds of watery tissue connecting them, one reaches a point where one is, once again, overwhelmed by a whole new world of complexity. And prior to that mechanical movement, there are the pattern circuits, the rivers that flow through in and out from the brain initiating and controlling that world.

Patterns are formed primarily through repetition, through habits, through a psychological response, through a feeling or emotion, through an accident and countless other incidents. An obstacle in the body initiates an alternative pattern and that continues until another obstacle initiates a counter pattern that may or may not intitiate a return to the original pattern. Patterns can be initiated mentally, physically, by accident, and by external manipulation. It could be thought of as movements in a liquid chess game.

Another person can often see other's patterns more clearly than the subject. This is simply because, once a pattern has been initiated, adherence to that pattern is what feels correct, comfortable. The body covers deviations instantly. When deviance has been accommodated in the body, one feels crooked when one is straight and straight when one is crooked.

The Upanisads and Ayur Vedic texts talk of 72,000 *nadis* running through the body. These have been translated as "veins." But there has not been any specific identification of the 72,000 except for about 10 of them that are associated with *prana*. In fact, they are better thought of as meridian lines. It seems meaningful to consider that these *nadis*, places where energy flows, are the patterns continually invoked in the body in movement. It is tempting to consider that the authors were referring by the massive numbers, to the infinite possibilities of different patterns running possible psycho-physical paths.

In view of this construction, what are the possibilities of doing something meaningful in yoga?

If patterns are formed primarily by habit, then the first thing we have to realize is that everything we have done by conscious effort, and everything that has happened to us, is imprinted in our bodies and impels us into our present movement-behaviour pattern. That is the base from which we work, the eye from which we see. Secondly, it is not going to make any difference what we are doing — walking, going to the toilet, doing yoga or reading a book — it is the habitual patterns in the body that determine our state and not the assumption of a particular position.

Our activities do have an effect on our bodies though. Yoga, for example, pulls major patterns into an alignment or balance. It ensures an energy flow through our main meridians. It balances us; it renews us.

But if we want to seriously and specifically penetrate into or assume a pattern complex, a baffle has to be construed to drive the energy into that particular channel. The baffle is construed by our conscious mind. But it has to be construed and placed in such a way that it is able to communicate with the unconscious mind — the autonomic nervous system — in effect, with everything else that we have ever done and thought and inherited. If it remained on the conscious level, it would only shorten the movement muscles into an action by means of the pattern and not intervene in the pattern. Needless to say, the chances of a successful consciously initiated alteration of a pattern complex are slim indeed. First the pattern has to be seen. The chances of seeing it are diminished since perception itself is altered by the pattern complex. As stated already, if your body is crooked, then when you are crooked you will feel straight and when you are straight, you will feel crooked. Secondly, a strategic placing, because it deals with a complex beyond our conscious control, is going to be difficult indeed. In fact, the most available way to deal with this is to throw the baffle out there haphazardly, like dice, and hope that it rolls in the way of a pattern. Obviously, only patience and persistence can be counseled. The successful penetration of a pattern complex is going to take time and it will depend on chance. There is almost nothing you can consciously do to control unconscious sequences except breathe.

It is not impossible to acquire mastery over these sequences. Every time that one does asanas, if one is working with awareness, one is observing, with body intelligence, more and more of the pattern of each movement. Of course, goal-oriented activity, desire to attain a particular end position, is going to overrule any possible observation, especially an observation with the shy body intelligence. Asanas are not about accomplishment. Accomplishment is about desire and desire works on the surface, connects directly to the surface muscle, even if its seed is virtually inaccessible. Awareness of a pattern can only be built up over a long period of time working with delicate intuitive attention. One can understand why humility is the key to all learning, the key to serious yoga. A failure to "see" reduces yoga to meaningless plagiaristic mimicry and ritual. But that is within the purview of choice. And then, as some form of grace, there are sudden flashes of insight that come from yoga itself.

It is very difficult to see oneself. This is the adage of the eye seeing the colour of the eye as it is looking through it. But it is necessary.

What help is available? Everyone is broadcasting his or her story all the time through his or her body. It is possible to see the patterns that others appropriate and work in their bodies and it is possible to intervene in those patterns effectively. An intervention in a particular pattern, by manipulation, sometimes as savage as a touch, done in a fraction of a second, at a critical juncture that the whole pattern radiates through, can initiate a pattern alteration that might have taken the subject person years to accomplish. A singular change in a pattern can have far reaching consequences for someone's body. It can change their life. It can spark changes that vibrate through the whole system. It is effective because it is actively and immediately incorporated into the balance co-ordination.

What manipulation or mobilization does, ideally, is to allow us to see beyond the limitations of our own pattern complexes. It challenges the death in our body. People have realizations from interventions in their body patterns that are both physical and mental. It provides a moment of insight that allows us to move beyond our knots, our dead spots — it is not as if something new is happening — everything is in place physically, the receptors have always been there, waiting for the pulse. The moment of realization is a recognition of our own possible selves.

And what about the morality of manipulation, of opening someone's body? Is it right to intervene in someone else's karma? As stated, giving an opening to someone is not giving them anything or doing anything to them. It is simply allowing them to realize their own body potential. It feels like something new. It is only assistance in throwing out unnecessary encumbrances and adhesions, baggage, that, stored and accumulated, causes limitation, pain. It is taking people beyond those constructed limitations that they often cherish. Many people feel uncomfortable with that. They only want to work in the comfort zones even when they are a source of chronic discomfort. They like their baggage. It comes down to choice. Everyone has to choose. But one is not a real teacher unless you can entice people to reach beyond their limitations.

The word "brahma" comes from the root *brnh* and it means to expand, to open and is taken to mean expansion without limit. Openings in the body feel good; they bring life to the body and the mind. They allow expansion of body and mind.

Most people want to know how to see these patterns and how to intervene. There is a massive amount of available information to be processed from each person that one has to work with. First of all, you have to touch people. But like a wine taster, you will be spitting out what you have drunk. You too are being examined when you touch someone. They know everything about you even though they may not know they know it. And then you have to bring up your intuition. You have to let your hands guide you. They can feel what is happening in each body. And all your own stories and desires are in your hands. They leak. Hands are as intimate and insidious a form of communion as eyes. Sometimes they work for the eyes. They are the connectors. And they have been abused. You have to be prepared to give of yourself with dispassion, generosity and joy. Anything else will be known for what it is. My old teacher, Mr. Rishi, told me that true learning is a communion of souls.

Pushing Buttons

"A push-button type of one-to-one correspondence does not exist and the cerebral motor area organizes responses by deftly adjusting and balancing between resultant external forces and the manifestations of inertia, constantly reacting to the proprioceptive signals and simultaneously integrating impulses from separate central subsystems, so that ten successive repetitions of the same movement demand ten successive impulses all different from each other."

NICHOLAI BERNSTEIN, *The Coordination and Regulation of Movements*

"There is nothing more dangerous than the death of our dreams."

PAASH

"The universities do not teach all things, so a doctor must seek out old wives, gypsies, sorcerers, wandering tribes, old robbers and such outlaws, and take lessons from them. A doctor must be a traveler. Knowledge is experience."

PARACELSUS

EXPERIENCE LEADS ME TO ASSUME that there are two basic paradigms of the self that are both subject and object of learning. Some people regard the self as a great mystery and use the world, their bodies, their conflicts, their learning to throw light on the mystery of the self. Others, ignoring that mystery, use those same things to hone or sharpen the self and use it as a tool to make their way through this world. Although it is possible to consider that these are not mutually exclusive, Sankara, in his introduction to the *Brahmasutram*, lays down the case for their mutual exclusivity. It comes down to the absolute exclusivity between subject and object.

If one chooses to uphold this absolute exclusivity, then it is possible to chart distinct processes of learning for each stream. Learning in the west has been primarily object related. Everything leads into the substantiality of the object. It is a concentration on materia. Indian learning, or at least traditional learning, all of which is metaphysical learning, uses the objective world for setting parameters for correct thinking. There is no objective determination — the goal of learning is merely correct thinking.

Correct thinking is the only possible preparation for revelation. Revelation is directly related to the subject being able to see himself or herself as he or she is. Revelation is a product of preparation, determination and, perhaps, chance.

Revelation is the only means of learning that can take you beyond the limitations of your own thinking. Nearly all thinking is body based. Body based knowledges have, by their very nature, an intuitive component that colours objectivity. The essential key to intuitive learning is humility.

The work in yoga asanas is in the space between the conscious and the unconscious mind. We are driven by habits, controlled by habits. We form our bodies around these habits. Asanas help us to become aware of these habits and through that awareness, to choose to honour them or exercise our independence from them. That means that serious work in yoga is going to be at the cutting edge of the comfort zone. It is going to be at the point of revelation of the ambiguous illusion/reality of limitation. When we confront restrictive habits, we often suffer pain. If the response is to retreat from pain, then one may be retreating from one's own limitations, and leaving them intact. Many people, becoming aware of a limitation, working through it and transcending it, experience joy. At the physical level, one can consider this an "opening." It is a contemplation of one of the body/mind knots.

Our habits are what we see through. They are the backdrop that forms our thinking, our perception at the "deep structure" level. Therefore we can understand that it is only humility that can allow us to gain an insight into what we are doing, what we are. It calls for the humility to abandon our cultured surfaces, our ornaments, our armours and comforts and thus the actions and reactions of our surface muscles. It is humility that allows us to make a little more of the unconscious conscious. And asanas, an internal body system of stretches, are the most refined of all spiritual disciplines, refined over thousands of years, that allow us to physically and practically approach those moments.

Pain is not necessarily gain. This idea probably came from Christianity where extreme pain is portrayed as an ultimate revelation. That same idea may be at the base of painful sexual rituals and obsessed devotions to various things. There is good pain and there is bad pain. Some pain shows you a pathway. It is useful because the body can mask pain. Other pain is a stop sign. But all pain is just another sensation. With yoga, you might be able to learn how to assess these limitations, how to exercise discrimination.

When you work with paralyzed people and they begin to feel pain, you know you are on the road. It is their first response. Our own limitations are like a paralysis, a knot in the body. We need pain recharged to reveal them to us as they have moved beyond our conscious control. The body bypasses and covers its knots and pains. Even though they are painful, they do not feel painful until revealed. They are invisible. Their sources are also invisible. They can be physical and/or mental. Sometimes when you remove the physical knot, a mental counter entity also disappears. A keen observer can notice the connection between them. Sometimes when a mental phenomenon departs, a physical knot also disappears. R.D. Laing wrote a book of poems entitled *Knots*. This is a book that everyone should read. It lays out that "unawareness of presuppositions" in popular behaviour that western culture is criticized for. It is a song of the west. It reveals the worship of our metaphysical reality in television soap operas on TV and in life. Knots are described exactly the same way in Sanskrit, as *granthas*. They are laid out in his poetry so that we can reminisce with gusto. It bridges the gap between our adoration of them and the silliness of that adoration.

The expression, "no pain no gain" is examined in Christian theological and bodybuilding metaphysics in the book *God's Gym* by Stephen Moore under the section of the same title on page 102. The implied promise here is that pain will effect a transformation. That illusion though, has already been followed through and whether one would consider it to have a future, is individual choice. It is the unwitting absolute adherence to this ancient ritual in our lives, behaviour and politics that is disturbing.

Yoga does take you beyond the limits of your own perception. If it does not do that, then it is mere commercial light exercise hopefully with a few mantras thrown in. Even that can work wonders. But there is really not much point in constructing another sentimentality cage around oneself. In the end, everything has to be shed and abandoned. And you do not want to feel deceived and weakened when its your time to molt, to shuffle off whatever needs to be abandoned. Yoga is letting go of things.

It is obvious that all of one's actions, one's past actions are revealed and used in any movement or asana. This is to say nothing of our thoughts, feelings and sensations that are also touched in every asana. Our past is what determines the present and the future. All of it is contained in our habits, what we perceive as our basic bodily reality usually in the form of a limitation. Asanas make it possible to intervene in that past, to neutralize it and change the future because they work on our basic unconscious habits that are the determinant of our fate revealed in our body movement, our thought patterns and feelings. They are a possible response of instant karma.

And as for our perception, Patanjali, in his great commentary on grammar says that one word, pronounced properly, is enough to take us to heaven. What he means is that, a word, looked at carefully, can be traced back to the desire to speak. It is a psycho-linguistic moment and he claims that that moment is the primal desire that started the vibration that led into the big bang. It is a moment of creation. He offers us a reflective insight into our origins, our beginning. What he is saying, is that full awareness of a single perception can lead us back to our origins through everything that has happened on the way. This is not a psychoanalysis based on free fantasy and recall, but intimately tied to our own body and its baggage. Asanas provide as intimate a tool as sound. An enthusiastic student of asanas just might set his sights on that primal vibration.

The implications are astounding. In every movement we can intuitively find its origins, our origins, its impediments, and the clear path through. Movement is the most accessible means of understanding and responding to our emotions, our sensations and our thinking.

Traditional Indian thought claims there are three powers (*saktis*) in us. There is a power of thinking (*jnanasakti*), a power of action (*karanasakti*) and a power of desire (*icchasakti*). They claim desire affects knowledge and action. Knowledge can affect action and action, knowledge. But desire is independent. Nothing touches it. It is a different area of the brain.

The Destroyer of Bridges

"…a lasting work of art — …the kind that remains in the heart as both a consolation and abiding challenge. Or an invitation: Let death come at the end of life, not the middle or the start. What all art finally means. Whatever means less than that…is just advertising or schlock.

What I see and feel for our…own art fall(s) far short of the visionary standards…where the primary life-impulse, imperfectly honoured or not, was a will to celebration, gratitude, and reverence, not to confiscation and control.

If the primary life-impulse in our society is a will to confiscation and control, its bound to get into our art.

The essential difference (between art and advertising)…(is that) art usually involves an invitation and solicits the entry and collaboration of the audience, while advertising usually implies a threat. …(A)rt invites you along any available road, while advertising dictates where you enter. And when.

Invitation as opposed to coercion."

STEVEN HEIGHTON, *The Admen Move on Lhasa*

YOGA IS AN ART. It is an art of the body. Not just on or of the body but the whole body. It is not, however, primarily an art that is connected with display. It is an art of seeing, as all serious art must be. Our body and mind are our first world. Seeing into the body and the mind means seeing, not with the eye of flesh, though that cannot be ruled out either since we need to use that, but seeing beyond that, using other senses and intuition that we might say belong to our body knowledge, our whole past history of our habits and culture, and even our genetic history.

If our aesthetic is really a personal sense of order, then the art of yoga is the awareness of our internal personal sense of order, our personal pattern that enables us to see.

The yoga sutras of Patanjali, indeed, all metaphysical schools ask us the same. They ask us to look back. This is indeed, the source of what we are now. Everything is embedded in our body and our mind. Science, art, metaphysics — they seek the same thing.

Being able to see this far implies something more than objective perception. It implies a form of vision as distinguished from perception. It implies an intuitive perception since what we want to perceive is not, at its vital moment, within the realm of objective perception.

Object perception is our way of navigating the world. But it is not the only means. All of our contemporary languages, and Sanskrit too, show an increase in nominalization. That means we are populating the world with objects. Vedic Seers saw the world in terms of moving patterns of energy. A noun was a temporary designation when a verbal energy embraced a particular form at a particular moment in time. Thus objects had many different names depending on the particular relation of the energy flow that absorbed them at that moment. This is embedded in the language. The tendency to turn outwards plagues all of our activity, mental and physical.

Indeed, the *Kathopanisad* verse reads:

पराञ्चिखानि व्यतृणत्स्वयम्भूस्तस्मात् पराङ्पश्यति नान्तरात्मन् ।
कश्चिद्धीरः प्रत्यगात्मानमैक्षद्व्व तन्न धुर मृतलबमिच्छन् ॥

"The self-existent pierced the senses outward, therefore one sees outward, not inside.
A certain wise man, desiring immortality, his eyes turned backwards, saw his own self directly."

The shifting of the perception of movement from the conscious to the unconscious, the making of the unconscious conscious, is the pathway of asanas. This is the pathway, the opportunity, the insight that asanas offer us. Asanas are the bridge and this is the meaning of the word yoga, from *yuj*, to join.

In a forthcoming paper of mine entitled "The Art Word," the etymologic origins of the word 'art' have been traced. Western etymologies trace the world back to Latin *ars artis*, which has references to decoration and entertainment. But Sanskrit can take us back further to the word *rta* which was one of the two forms of truth from vedic times. *Satya* was the word for objective truth. But *rta* was the word for truth as it applies to the whole moving cosmos, truth as relative to the whole. This sense of truth is what must be considered for art if we are to take our art seriously and it applies to our yoga as well. Penetrating the unconscious in the intimate way that it is done in yoga is a realization of our individual consciousness as much larger than us as an individual; it is a consistent and systematic realization of the self as a universal soul, all life.

In the British period, yoga was reduced to street entertainment of fakirs and yogic tricks. Later, it was linked to sex and drugs — a pre-occupation of Christian civilizations everywhere. But there are older links than this – even the terminology and exemplification in vedanta are from the *jaduvalla* or magician traditions. And what yoga has become in our own time is equally fantastic.

The traditional Indian education system was not linked to economics. It was a system that was based entirely on individual learning and accomplishment (see my paper "The Memory Eye" in (*Journal of Indian Philosophy* 14, 1986). The organization into mass education, based on economics has led ultimately, because of a failure to maintain a balance in favour of learning as opposed to economics, in the direction of the destruction of education. But this should not be a surprise — we only have to review what has happened to plants, birds, learning, and languages, to understand this.

A similar pattern has emerged within the yoga tradition. Yoga has, for perhaps the first time, become a mass movement in the world accessible and desirable to ordinary people. It has been subjected to the commodification necessary to make it a product. The unique products that have arisen from that are the class formats, props, the teacher training, the packages, the objectification placement fetishes, the advertising, the cheap symbol-oriented spirituality, dogmatic group social rituals and so on.

There are more people susceptible to advertising and dogma than there are with body sensitivities. Our governments and education have taught us that business is first.

There are very few people connected with yoga in the world today that can invite us into the world of yoga anymore, or for that matter, the world of art. Even through language, filtered through western academia for a thousand years, we are unable to assign a serious meaning to the word art in spite of having records of great artists who have actively participated in the truth of art and left their pathway record icons. The distinction between invitation and coercion is obliterated.

One of the small mantras recited at the initiation of a learning process in India goes:

सह नाववतु ।
सह नौ भुनक्तु ।
सह वीर्यंकरवावहै ।
तेजस्विनावधीतमस्तु
मा विद्विषावहै ।
ॐ ग्यानिःग्यानिःग्यानिः ॥

"May he help us both
May he enjoy us both
May we become inspired together
Let us both possess brilliance
Let us not hate
Om Peace Peace Peace"

The buzz word for art, irrespective of its suitability is "beauty." But the meaning that we take from looking back through words is "truth in relation to the whole moving cosmos." And this applies to yoga as well. When we get a sense of that truth, things are beautiful. It has to do with harmony, transcendence, a quietness of body and mind.

Business is and has been a bulldozer thriving on destruction. Lately, it is not honest trade, it is an incarnation of the demon of greed. It does not crush only material but languages, the means of feeling communication between people...bridges. The demon of greed, the *krtimukha*, devoured everything it could get its eyes on and then it devoured its own body. As such, castrated, it protects against the evil eye.

Its bound to get into our yoga.

a precision fetish

W HEN I WROTE *The Yoga Tradition of the Mysore Palace*, I noted that the direction one would have expected the yoga practice-tradition to go would be towards increased precision. This was a rational expectation that came from examining the past history of other Indian philosophical traditions and spiritual disciplines and the direction of the popular movement. A creative moment in lineal development can only last so long. A plethora of detail commonly follows to substantiate, consolidate and/or validate the instant where that creative moment occurred. In respect of increased precision, there were multiple new fields for yoga practice to draw on — body cultures from very different parts of the world, different body disciplines and the tradition of yoga itself — also multidisciplinary, because the present tradition itself was bound up with the Indian wrestler tradition, western gymnastics, possibly military exercise systems and so on. In addition, the western world, from which the main impetus to growth and exploration had come, because of the colonial situation and economic factors, brought new theories of movement that came from modern dance, physiotherapy and philosophical reflections on movement. Lately, ideas that derived from Chinese theories that possibly came from India originally, have begun to weave their ways back into the contemporary thought and tradition. Over and above this, there has been influence of massage schools from Europe, Japan, China, Thailand and other places that have become appreciated, effective and influential perspectives on the body.

The elements that arise from the clash of different cultures are often extraordinary creations that embarrass both cultures for a long period of time. Usually, neither is able to acknowledge these creations. The exploration in new points of view and materials often leads to growth in unexpected directions, as, for example, architecture and furniture. One would expect that this would be a threat to tradition, but my experience is that tradition is vital and that this actually represents growth and change within tradition that is necessary for its survival.

If we examine carefully the direction of the movement towards precision, a rather interesting picture emerges. In many European countries, unique yogic ideas of stretching have been incorporated into mainstream medical and physiotherapeutic practices over a period of years but not marketed under the name of yoga. In North America, physiotherapy, oriented towards repetitive machine practice, has not incorporated such ideas. Any therapeutic influences of yoga have come in the strong alternative medicine area. Yoga practice, however, has drawn on physiotherapeutic anatomy and movement research and drawn a certain amount of that into yoga practice. In Europe, it has been yoga practice as practice that has been strongest. In North America, yoga practice overlaid by a popular spirituality and marketing thrust has been strongest. And, as might be expected, the mechanical aspects of movement have been at the forefront of evaluation of yogic movement, for example, in the scope of critique of certain movements like inversions. It should also be mentioned that yoga has not renewed itself on the basis of Chinese medicine that might have been a base formerly. Chinese medicine theory has been the basis of much renewal in alternative medicines and chiropractory in North America.

In North America, after the initial introduction, one of the primary thrusts in the popularization of yoga has been business marketing. The spiritual overlay has been very important for marketing as it can promise psychological benefits like peace of mind, freedom from stress and harmony and makes for infallible promotion. It can provide a social environment. That social environment can replace personal individual responsibility; certainly a situation that is attractive to people who are unhinged by the increasing alienation in our society because of age, hostile work places, loss of societal comfort and a paucity of social and cultural skills. When this progresses into a situation where it is necessary to exclude, it is called a cult. This provides a unique marketing possibility and has been exploited for years.

On the object side of marketing, props for doing yoga, classes, retreats, books, special sessions and so on form the main corpus and are marketed in North America through publications like *The Yoga Journal* and small local publications. In fact, the Internet, rather than being a provider of information on yoga, provides marketing and advertising opportunities.

On the other hand, in North America, yoga has been strong in the alleviation of stress. In Europe, where stress is managed in a different way, yoga has responded to the physical element in treatment of stress related injuries. Indeed, Gert Van Leeuwen has published specifically on that (*Stop RSI*). In North America, treatment has focused on a state of mind brought about by working with yoga both with meditation and related physical work. That has led in the psycho-spiritual direction. It is a tendency towards a meditational complex that is, to a large extent, external to the body. It is interesting that the Lonavla yogic hospital was strong in the use of *pranayama*, breathing, for treatment of ailments.

It is thus possible to see the North American direction of yoga, taking up the urge towards precision, as part of a marketing system that operates on the basis of control through advertising and through indoctrination to objectify and produce marketable products. There has always been a puritan imperative in North America.

However, the drive towards precision is part of other forces as well. In teaching asanas, precision in movements, a part of learning has been developed as a form of mimicry. More than that, it has been objectified as an absolute that does not account for individual variations of body or skill in

Coventry University

Lanchester Library
Tel 02476 887575

Borrowed Items 01/08/2017 13:56
XXXXXX8782

Item Title	Due Date
3800100609820	22/08/2017
* Yoga touchstone	

Amount Outstanding: £2.00

* Indicates items borrowed today
Thankyou for using this unit
www.coventry.ac.uk

accomplishment. The asana position is something to be mimicked and strived for rather than used to explore the limitations of one's own body. If the asana had remained as a means of exploring one's own limitations in the body that accrued from habit and various things, then there would be no external asana standard as such. In other words, the asana, as a precise object, rather than a means, is on the way to becoming a quantifiable and thus mass marketable object. This is observable in the absolute imperative enunciated in regard to asanas in most contemporary schools. This insistent evaluation is not something that comes from inside, from exploration; it is a mimicked position imposed externally. It makes yoga meaningless. It serves domination complexes and thus control. The drive to precision has become obsessed linear thinking.

Further, there is extensive use of props to bring people into what is considered a better position. Although props can have value — they can be used to enable people to explore areas that they would not have access to, the tendency is to use them to make the asana look better. For example, the extensive padding put under the shoulders in *sarvangasana*. A minimal amount of padding is helpful in *sarvangasana* as the neck is slightly concave and it ensures that he neck is not stretched straight. When additional padding is put under the shoulders, it is to give the shoulders height so that the back can be used more effectively, so that it can assume its natural straightness because it is not impinged by the shoulders and the shoulder blades. But that means the restrictive areas are not challenged. They are bypassed. To do this is tantamount to giving a raised shoe to someone who has scoliosis when one leg is shorter than the other. It looks better. They can walk without any trace of a limp and the twist in the body is less obvious. The only problem is that it drives the scoliosis curve further into the spine. While nothing can be done about a structural scoliosis, it acquires more territory around itself and draws that in as well. All of that space in the body is lost and if the raised shoe is used, that area, instead of being challenged, goes on to acquire even more territory. The structural scoliosis attains an increased functional component. I see props being used in that way habitually rather than as a means to explore dead spaces. They actually create dead spaces in people's bodies. They are cosmetic rather than therapeutic. An insight has become a crutch. And there are vested interests in crutches.

This calls for further examination into the teaching of yoga itself. Have the great teachers become gurus? Like gurus, even in this age of economic enlightenment, their word is unquestionable. They have metaphysically raised the stakes so that no disagreement would be possible. Originally this phenomenon was part of tantric discourse teaching. The idea was to raise the level of the argument until no disagreement was possible — one transcends in unity. Zen Koans have similar functions but approach from a different point of view. Disagreement, doubt, would mean a religious faux pas. This is easy to see in the *Bhagavad Gita*, where Krishna keeps telling his friend, Arjuna that, on this matter, there is no doubt. No matter that the *Bhagavad Gita* has been referred to as a right wing document enhancing the status quo of the caste system and its contingencies by Ambedkar. Should that make us suspicious? A keen student of yoga might like to examine the precision complex more carefully. Is the urge towards precision something that comes from inside that student as part of his exploration, or is it part of a move towards control on another's part? Confiscate and control? In other words, has the movement towards precision, instead of coming from a desire from inside, from intuitive understanding, been co-opted, made into an object/desire complex, made marketable, and been used to affirm the usual dominance-submission complex? Does it contribute to delusion rather than remove it?

If it is an attempt to grab control, then the urge to precision, to refinement and understanding, has become a rather unwelcome fetish. Something beneficial has been transformed into something rather insidious.

It's an old process. We need not be surprised. It has happened before. Are asanas comparable then to a pair of red high heels? Are they just another billboard hoarding on the road to enlightenment? Have the admen already moved in — have they been on the road for a long time? Have they already brought their friends, the lawyers and the politicians?

Traditional Learning

योगेन योगो ज्ञातव्यो योगो योगात्प्रवर्तते ।
योऽप्रमत्तस्तु योगेन स योगे रमते चिरम् ॥

"Yoga should be known through yoga. Yoga arises from yoga.
Whoever is honest with yoga will enjoy in yoga for a long time."

Quoted by VYASA under yoga sutra 3.6

LEARNING IN INDIA — at least traditional learning — is based upon a metaphysical knowledge system. All knowledge systems, whether grammar, yoga, dance, music or logic follow this pattern or are deeply influenced by it. This system of learning is distinctly different from the western system of learning. The western system of learning is oriented towards objectivity. Objectivity is the inner child of science, the darling or demon child of materia. But Indian systems of learning took subjectivity into account. Their aims, as such, were to use objective criteria fully, but only as a stepping-stone into what was beyond that. They taught the means to correct knowledge. They were a guide to correct knowledge. Correct knowledge, being ultimately subjective, was the seeker's individual responsibility. Thus, even today, in traditional sastric schools, a degree was not a certification as in the west; it was an indication that you were adequately prepared to pursue knowledge through some particular configuration.

I have outlined earlier in a paper called "The Memory Eye" (*Journal of Indian Philosophy* 14, 1986) the traditional Indian learning system. I review that here in two aspects: grammar and music.

A child to be learned in Sanskrit will begin by memorizing the *Amarakosa*, a Sanskrit poetic dictionary and Panini's grammar at the age of about 4. As he begins to learn more Sanskrit, which entails memorizing all the basic verb and noun paradigms he will turn to the study of grammar. In memorization, sequences are important. One thing is connected to another. If one forgets some particular thing, one does not search but enters somewhere in the sequence and waits for it to appear. Further, one does not try to remember but stills the mind and lets the item appear on its own. For the study of grammar, he will begin the study of the *Siddhanta Kaumudi*. This is a text that teaches how to use the grammar. Instead of rote memory, but making use of that rote memory, he will learn how to derive each word by applying the rules of the grammar. Indeed, even though this is analytical in process, there is a strong rote memory component in that. This is directly correlated to an objective output. There is a balance between the analytic logic and drawing the required item from inside as learned in the acquisition of memory items. Then, after years of working that system, his mind will turn to the grammar as a whole. The mind begins a synthetic function which is often critical of the grammar but from the point of view of the whole grammar. It is not the analytical objective critique that we find in western scholarship which examines the object independent of its whole context.

I have likened these stages in learning to the three final limbs of yoga as mentioned in Patanjali. The first stage is *dharana*, holding the mind on some particular object. The second stage is *dhyana*, the beginning of thought or reflection on that object, absorption, meditation. The third stage is *samadhi*, the full coming together of the mind on that object with all its implications, or the ability to see fully that object in relation to the whole, isolated in that context.

In the case of music, in South India, a student will begin learning the notes and then particular sequences of notes. This requires sustained practice and demanding accuracy. Then they learn to sing some devotional songs. Then they will begin the study of *varnams*. *Varnams* are complete basic raga formations in miniature and they are practiced in different speeds. A raga is a particular musical sequence of a particular ascending and descending scale with restrictions as to emphasis and note sequence. It is learned as an abstract musical problem. But each raga has one or more accompanying songs that are set to time. In the performance of a raga, the alapana, usually the first part, is an examination of that musical form and it is totally improvisational and personal. The raga structure is so well known that it is elaborated according to the mood and feeling of the musician at that moment. Thus, each time, it is a total fresh creation. It is not learned as a musical sequence but elaborated from within and coloured by the musician's emotion, his or her state of mind and feeling, his rapport with the audience and so on.

In these methods of learning, at each step along the way, the student is taught to look inside. The objective correlates, while a definite part of that knowledge complex, are subsumed to an intuitive understanding that is innovative and accurate. There is no linear accumulation of knowledge but a deep surrender to and examination of patterns that form a creative meditation object. Each absorption in that pattern leads to further revelation.

Learning in yoga has never been as developed as in grammar and music mainly because there has not been a well-defined tradition. These two examples were chosen to illustrate an objective purpose and a creative purpose. In fact, there is no difference between the two. It is western thought that has separated them; like it has separated religion and life.

Most students of yoga seem to stop after mimicking a few particular forms. They cease even to acquire forms to mimic. These forms are a key to discover patterns running through the body. They are the means of refining movement, of confining it to the places where it actually occurs in its most pure form, of working into the body, through the muscles and connective tissue to the very signals that enable the body to flow like a river. Insight, turned inwards, can reveal the patterns, the categories through which we see.

Traditional learning, even though non-acquisitive, is ego related in a different relationship. Acquisitive knowledge leads to the idea that one collects and possesses objects. It is attractive to the hunter-gatherer mentality. It is a connection that leads to the social possession of trinkets. But traditional knowledge, since it is something that is individually body related does not have that element. It develops a different area of the brain. It uses the tension between one's self and one's accoutrement collection to reveal more of one's self. People who have learned in a traditional manner usually do not know what they know until they come into contact with others against whom their own understanding is thrown into contrast. Of course, there can be no competition between someone who is mimicking an external form and someone who has an internal body knowledge understanding of that form and uses that to explore their own body. Trinket collectors might be raucous with verbal eloquence but people who have learned traditionally understand what they know and what they do not know.

> "Well, to have had the privilege of knowing an old tradition.
> It has been, I think, decisive in my own life."

LEONARD COHEN

पृथ्व्यपेजोनिलखे समुत्थिते पञ्चात्मके योगगुणे प्रवृत्ते ।
न तस्य रोगो न जरा न मृत्युः प्राप्तस्य योगाग्निमयं शरीरम् ॥

When the fivefold qualities of yoga has been produced,

Arising from earth, water, fire, air and space,

no sickness then, old age or death comes to him

who has obtained a body in the fire of yoga.

Svetasvataropanisad 2.12

Yoga and Art

A DISTILLATION OF THE HAPPINESS THAT MODERN TECHNOLOGY HAS PRODUCED is Joseph Lanza's definition of public music which he called called Elevator Music in his book of the same title.

Geeta Kapur, trying to define the oriental aesthetic in terms of hindustani music, called it "the vibrations of a shuddering soul in a vastly spiraling melancholy."

Inayat Khan, the Sufi been player, said "Music is nothing less than the picture of our Beloved. It is because music is the picture of our Beloved that we love music…If only we would listen to the voice of all the beauty that attracts us in any form, we would find that in every aspect it tells us that behind all manifestations is the perfect Spirit, the spirit of wisdom."

Joseph Albers, speaking of colour, said "to honor the masters creatively is to compete with their attitude rather than with their results, to follow an artistic understanding of tradition — that is, to create, not to receive."

"When he claims to be solitary, the artist lulls himself in a perhaps fruitful illusion, but the privilege he grants himself is not real. When he thinks he is expressing himself spontaneously, creating an original work, he is answering other past or present, actual or potential, creators. Whether one knows it or not, one never walks alone along the path to creativity."

CLAUDE LEVI STRAUSS, *The Way of the Masks*

We have mentioned earlier that yoga is an art. Indeed, as a quest for truth, yoga is intimately realized as an art. The word art derives from the Sanskrit *rta* as mentioned and comes to mean truth. A quest for truth has to take everything into account. Mechanistic formulations, economic constraints and rituals, personal ego support, educational formulas and so on are abstractions that serve other masters. Humility serves nothing but truth. It is not a useful product for this world as it is, but a necessary ingredient for accurate perception.

51

When we think of the arts, we think of creativity. And the ideas of creativity have a rather different history. In the first place, the idea of novelty is predominant in ideas of creativity. But this is to subscribe to a very limited worldview and it is a political decision. The ancient world believed in cyclical time. The Judaeo Christian world perpetrated the myth of lineal time. The most striking manifestation of this is the birth of Jesus; divinity is born directly into time and suffers its consequences. In this process, there is a cultural shift. Instead of looking to the past for the future, it becomes necessary to shift people's allegiances to the future itself. This is done emotionally by making the idea of novelty prominent and rationally by making the idea of progress prominent.

But "creativity" came to take on larger dimensions. Not only was the idea of novelty a necessary element of aesthetic appreciation, but it became part of the mythology as well. "Creative," in time, comes to mean "creating out of nothing." This is in imitation of God who came down and created the world in seven days. This was novel. It is only in the sixteenth or seventeenth century that this idea achieves full prominence. In our own day, we can see its strength in the absolutist ideas of the abstract expressionists and in the teaching rigour of our art schools. In the art schools, students are told to forget about materials, forget about skills, techniques and history — they should just somehow "get creative." They too, like God, might create something out of nothing. They are told that traditional skills and so on will limit their creative expression, therefore they should be regarded with suspicion.

It is possible to look further back into the word "create" just as it was possible to do with the word art. The word "create" comes from the Sanskrit root *kr* which means "to make" or "do." It implies a materialistic or craft base that is in contradistinction to the meaning we are so familiar with, creation out of nothing. In fact, we see creativity as an objective component that people possess or do not possess. And we tend to see it as something that is connected only with what we consider traditional forms of art. But even those forms of art that we consider traditional are severely limited. In Indian thought, war is considered a man's art. The learning of language is considered an art.

And if we think of "creative" in art, the tendency is to think that something entirely new is in front of us. But even simple logic should determine that, if there was something that was absolutely new in front of us, we would have no classification scheme to qualify it with. It would be out of the range of our conceptual power and perhaps, perceptual capability. What we really mean when we say that something is new, a product of creativity, is that it differs just slightly from the norm so that we can recognize the norm and also the deviation. In other words, it belongs to the past, but a past that we choose to consider as non-existent. We see the object as new, not as belonging to the past. We deceive ourselves into taking on the grandeur of total novelty and creativity at the very moment that we retreat into the safety of our own conceptions.

But creativity is the basis of all life, from evolution to emotion. Creativity is what makes life meaningful.

We have seen yoga as an introspection of the patterns through the body. Traditionally the affects of the body are considered to extend 14 finger widths beyond it as well — an aura that arises from the body. And we have seen how the mind, with its rationale and emotion, is an intimate part of the movement complex and how each movement vibrates through the body in a myriad of possible paths.

Yoga, which literally means "connecting," through its repeated and sustained movements is grounded in the physical and exploring the psychic and autonomic participation in each movement. All of those components are the colour of the eye that we desire to see as we look through it. Yoga is something that continually turns inward; it attempts to refine a movement, reduce it to that vital moving part. It is an art of exploration and it is grounded absolutely in the first world, the body.

But the exploration differs from our usual approaches. If we reflect how obvious it is to us that "everything's connected" we can perhaps understand some of the significance of a system of thought and movement that bases itself on this. The western approach has been reductive and mechanistic. Freud is perhaps the crowning glory of this movement. The basic idea in Freud, as in medicine in general, was that if you could isolate, observe and classify, you could be free of or perhaps control something from that. Yoga, instead, is an art of synthesis. It is not that abstraction does not have its place, but its place is subordinate to the ability to synthesize, to see the whole.

What do we mean when we talk of creativity being stimulated from yoga? First of all, yoga grounds the mind in the body. Everything is relevant to the body. All of our intelligence is body based whether we recognize it or not. Maxine Sheets-Johnstone in *The Roots of Thinking* traces the evolutionary connection of our intelligence through that to communication and pleasure. If we think of creativity in the light of its word origin, what yoga does first is gives us an inner mobility. It gives us a mobility that is not based on muscle contraction. It is in the body — in the tissues, the skin, the reach of the breath and so on. This movement does not lead to a sense of accomplishment but to a deep emotional satisfaction, a transcendent pleasure without an object. It is harmonious with one's own body, inside. This inner harmony gives one the sense that anything is possible in a physical context. It is a state of non-interference because a form of balance is found. It is a state of quiet concentration, of total receptivity. Because it wipes the slate clean, one can start over without external conceptions. It enables one to reach a state beyond the "learned" categorization of the outside world. It puts us in touch with our own selves. It allows us to see. The Sanskrit word that comes closest to this concept is the word *pratibha*. This means literally to illuminate, cast light upon, enlighten. By secondary extraction, it means to see via that illumination. *Pratibha* though, means more than creativity. It has a sense of inspiration. Again, to refer to the etymological sense of the English term, inspire means to breathe in, to take a deep breath.

Movement itself, like the idea of "make" or "do" from the root *kr*, is what gives access to different parts of the brain that are often locked to other forms of perception. Like the movement of the hand with a pencil, akin to a spirit possession, leading us somewhere beyond our conscious self, so the movement in asanas touches on our emotions, our thinking, our history and our very being.

If we think of our aesthetic in art as our personal sense of order, then we can think of yoga as being at the root of that. It is yoga that gives us access to our personal sense of order that is manifested in our art no matter what form that art.

This creative act is the only bulwark we have against the overwhelming pollution of objectivity.

An agama text defines art thus:

$$\text{कर्तृशक्तिं व्यञ्जयति कला ।}$$

"Art (is what) reveals the power (sakti) of the artist (maker)."

Yoga reveals our natural power to us. It helps us participate in our creativity, our life, almost at an objective level.

The realization of the creative component of yoga is not verbally accessible. You know it through doing it. Either you know it or you do not know it or you might know it and not know it. There is no other way.

> "…On each occasion one should honour the sect of the other, for by doing so one increases the influence of one's own sect and benefits that of the other; while by doing otherwise one diminishes the influence of one's own sect and harms the other. Again whosoever honours his own sect or disparages that of another, wholly out of devotion to his own, with a view to showing it in a more favourable light, harms his own sect even more seriously. Therefore, concord is to be commended, so that men may hear one another's principles and obey them…"

Twelfth Major Rock Edict of the Mauryan emperor, ASOKA, inscribed in the third century BC.

यदा चर्मवदाकाशं वेष्टयिष्यन्ति मानवाः।
तदा देवमविज्ञाय दुःखस्यान्तो भविष्यति ॥

When men shall roll up space like a piece of skin —
Then there will be an end of the misery that comes from not knowing god.

Svetasvataropanisad 6:20

photographs

The following photographs of Sri Dattatreya were taken in Mysore in the royal graveyards, on Chamundi hill, in the temples at Halebid and Somanathpur, in Japan, and in Sweden at Villa Adelsten in Stockholm, the Bergianska Tradgard and other parts of Brunnsviken. Six of the photographs have previously appeared in *Namaskar*.

"As voluntary control is overriding in slow movements, it is liable in this case to interefere with the primitive reflex control and prevent the movement from being carried out in the natural, organic, and efficient way. Our awareness must discern this organic need. Such discernment is perhaps the truest 'knowledge of self.'"

MOSHE FELDENKRAIS, *Awareness through Movement*

inversions

adhomukhavrksasana

pincamayurasana

sayanasana

sirsasana

parsvasirsasana

parivttaikapadasirsasana

ekapadasirsasana

parsvaikapadasirsasana

urdhvapadmasirsasana

pindasirsasana

urdhvaparsvapadmasirsasana

parivrttavirasirsasana

parivrttavirasirsasana

niralamabanasirsasana

sarvangasana

ekapadasarvangasana

baddhapadmasarvangasana

Standing Asanas

vrksasana

trikonasana

parivrttatrikonasana

parsvakonasana

parivrttaparsvakonasana

parivrttaparsvakonasana

virabhadrasana

virabhadrasana

virabhadrasana

virabhadrasana

virabhadrasana

virabhadrasana

Forward Bends

baddhakonasana

pascimottanasana

pascimottanasana

triangmukhaikapadapascimottanasana

maricyasana

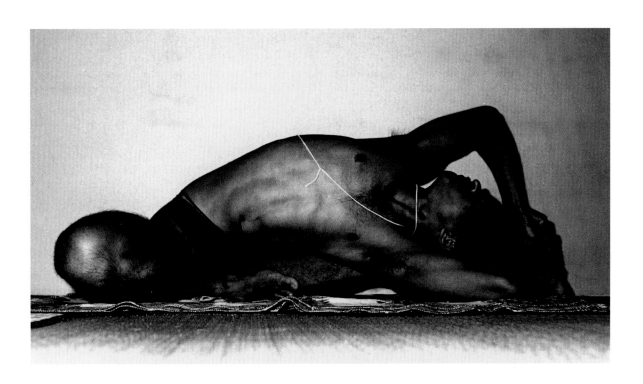

parivrttapascimottanasana

uttanapascimottanasana

ekapadasirsasana

ekapadasirsasana

bhairavasana

cakorasana

skandasana

durvasana

dvipadasirsasana

dvipadasirsasana

yoganidrasana

malasana

yogadandasana

upavistakonasana

trivikramasana

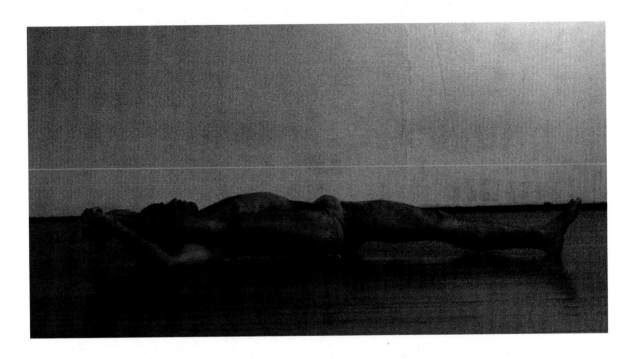

suptatrivikramasana

samakonasana

hanumanasana

vasisthasana

visvamitrasana

kasyapasana

kalabhairavasana

Balancings

bakasana

parsvabakasana

ekapadapurvabakasana

ekapadordhvabakasana

kukkutasana

parsvakukkutasana

tittibhasana

dvipadakaundinyasana

parivartanayantrakaundinyasana

saptasaptacatvarimsatkaundinyasana

ekapadagalavasana

dvipadagalavasana

Back Bends

urdhvadhanurasana

urdhvadhanurasana

ekapadordhvadhanurasana

kapotasana

laghuvajrasana

mahavajrasana

ekapadarajakapotasana

ekapadarajakapotasana

ekapadarajakapotasana

ekapadarajakapotasana

ekapadarajakapotasana

ekapadarajakapotasana

rajakapotasana

dhanurasana

dhanurasana

dhanurasana

ekapadaviparitadandasana

ekapadaviparitadandasana

vrscikasana

vrscikasana

vrscikasana

vrscikasana

gandabherundasana

gandabherundasana

natarajasana